Sky Talk

Philip Hogge

G-ASGC

BOAC

Burnt Ash Publishing

First published in Great Britain in 2020

Burnt Ash Publishing
A division of Burnt Ash Developments Limited
86-90 Paul Street
London
EC2A 4NE

Copyright © 2020 by Philip Hogge
Printed by T J International
Typeset in Bookman Old Style, titles in Impact, captions in Acumin

ISBN 978-1-9162161-5-0

A CIP Catalogue for this book is available from the British Library

Contents

Introduction

This collection of short stories comes from my abiding love of aviation. It all began when, aged eight or nine, I discovered aeroplanes. A light aircraft, an Auster I think, made a forced landing in a field near where we lived in Devon — that must have been somewhere around 1950. I was enthralled. Like so many pilots, I started by building model aircraft made of balsa and tissue paper, powered by elastic bands and small diesel engines. This was followed by a gliding course with the Air Cadets in 1958 and an RAF Flying Scholarship while still at school. During one rapturous summer holiday in 1959, Yvonne Pope taught me to fly a Tiger Moth and I gained my Private Pilot's Licence.

Looking back after all these years, I know I owe her so much. She was a kindly, dedicated instructor who demanded high standards, instilling the right attitude of mind. Flying is fun — but — you must treat it with the greatest of respect and care; if you don't, it will turn round and bite you!

Airline flying in the 1960s was not as it is now. There was still an element of glamour, adventure and excitement. I was lucky enough to start with BOAC on the Britannia 312, seeing the last of the propeller operations across the North Atlantic. In 1964, I converted to the VC10 and from there progressed (or was it regressed?) to the Boeing 707 and finally to the mighty 747.

Throughout that time, I remained dedicated to the cause of flight safety, good airmanship and helping others achieve the same. And I know it was Yvonne who pointed me in that direction.

A few years ago, I tried to write some memoirs, but stopped because I did not want to break confidences or embarrass old colleagues. Instead, I felt short stories would capture better the ambiance of those times. The first piece which follows is factual, the rest are all fictional stories, but based on things I've either done, known about, read about or have adapted from other people's tall stories. Most are amalgams of various characters I have known — suitably disguised.

I hope they evoke the airline world I knew from the 1960s to the 1990s.

Acknowledgements

I owe a huge debt of gratitude to the late Walter Wells, emeritus professor of English at California State University, Dominguez Hills, who inspired me and sparked the desire to write. Also, I must thank Jan Thomas for her constructive criticism; and my wife, Caroline, for listening to endless aviation talk, correcting my English, improving my punctuation and making so many very helpful suggestions.

Good friends and colleagues have also helped with encouragement, new ideas and by ensuring technical accuracy. They are: Peter Benest, Nev Boulton, Hugh Dibley, Alex Fisher, Jelle Hieminga, David Hyde, Peter Kirtley, Gwyn Mullett, Alan Murgatroyd, John Richards, Mike Riley, Calvin Shields, Frank Tallis, Hugh Tweed, Keith Warburton, Chris White and Steve Zerkowitz. I thank you all.

Credits

The publishers are very grateful to British Airways, BAE Systems, Imperial War Museum, Ministry of Defence, NATS Holdings, BBC, Smithsonian National Air and Space Museum, Jelle Hieminga, Mick Baxter, Bob Parrick and many others for their help and cooperation, as well as the use of their photographs, along with other information and data.

The Vickers VC10 was popular with pilots and passengers alike (Mick Baxter).

Flying the Vickers VC10 through Africa

I flew VC10s from 1964 to 1978 and look back on those days with fond memories. This is a factual article I wrote for a website, put together by Jelle Hieminga, called *A little VC10derness* (www.vc10.net). It describes the fun and some of the challenges of flying in the 1960s and 1970s on the African routes for which the VC10 was designed.

I was on the first Hamble intake to join BOAC in 1962, converting to VC10s in 1964. This was my first jet type and, looking back, I realise now how lucky I was, not only to fly this magnificent aircraft, but also to do so on such an extensive route structure, first to West Africa, and then to the rest of Africa, the Far East, the Americas and across the Pacific to Australia.

In the early 1960s, the world had not changed so much from pre-war days, and, except in the United States and a few other places, high-rise buildings were the exception. Dubai, for example, was still a small trading station on a creek in the desert with wooden dhows drawn up on the strand. The crew hotel was one of the tallest buildings in town, all of about four or five storeys — a far cry from the 'Las Vegas' it has become today.

I have few exciting tales to tell, most of my memories are of the wonder of being able to explore much of the world before it became homogenised. Of all these memories, flying through Africa is perhaps the most intense.

Communications were, by modern standards, primitive (overseas telephone calls had to be pre-booked several hours ahead), HF (high frequency) radio communications could be hit and miss, navigation aids frequently did not work, airfield lighting was sometimes only partly available, meteorological reports could be highly dubious (it was better to ask the BOAC station officer to look out of the window and tell you what he saw than to rely on the official weather observation) and en route ATC (air traffic control) was often 'do it yourself'. When away from London, you were very much on your own with no instant data link back to head office — far more fun, if somewhat less efficient.

Most of the captains I first flew with were either ex-Imperial Airways or ex-RAF bomber pilots. Their stories of flying boats through Africa told of a magical mix of flying, 'seafaring', night stops in lonely staging posts on rivers and lakes, and low sightseeing over vast herds of wild game. The ex-RAF people, understandably, had less to say, some of their experiences being too harrowing to tell except after many beers. But all felt that flying was 'not what it was', a feeling that exists in every generation, including my own.

The VC10 was designed for the hot, high, short runways of the African routes. Therefore, it had an excellent take-off performance, a little over-powered from an accountant's point of view, but much enjoyed by us pilots. It was a real pilot's aircraft; lots of performance, precise powerful controls, very stable and with an ability to flatter even the most ham-fisted pilot. It also had a roomy, well laid out flight deck, with large windows giving good visibility, and a legendarily quiet cabin.

But it was Africa that captured my heart. Flying south from Cairo towards Khartoum along the Nile, you could see this thin green ribbon stretching far out ahead, winding like a huge S-bend through the vast brown desert, first far out to the eastern horizon towards Luxor and Aswan, then back underneath near Wadi Halfa, only to disappear in the west towards Dongola, returning once again to wind its way east towards Atbara, and finally to Khartoum. This was, indeed, to see one of the wonders of the natural world.

I have always been fascinated by exploration, and having read about the Victorian explorers — Burton, Speke, Grant and others — searching for the source of this mysterious river, and now seeing it with my own eyes really drove home the modern wonders of jet travel. Whereas they had sweated and struggled, here was I, comfortably sitting in my shirt sleeves, taking the same journey in a matter of hours. I remember once, later, when I became a captain, going through the cabin to talk to the passengers after a long delay in Rome on our way to Nairobi, and being accosted by an irate lady passenger who was upset by being only a few hours late. She was most unimpressed when I pointed out that the journey we were now making in little more than six hours would have taken her over six months only 100 years earlier.

In the 1960s, when daily services were a rarity, we had many days off at slip stations. There was time to explore: to hire horses in Cairo and ride out into the desert to see the stepped pyramids at Saqqara; or to go sailing in Khartoum on the Blue Nile from the Blue Nile Sailing Club whose club house was the Melik, Kitchener's gunboat, built in 1896 and used at the relief of Khartoum in 1898. There was time to hire cars and drive out from Nairobi up the Rift Valley to Naivasha, and then north around Mount Kenya via Gilgil, Nakuru, Thomson's Falls, Nanuki, Meru, Embu and Fort Hall. On one memorable trip, we hired a car in Kampala and drove to Murchison Falls and Lake Albert, arriving just after a thunderstorm had passed. The sky was dark blue-black, the earth and trees newly washed and sparkling clean. There was no one around, the only sign of human existence being a low pipe rail fence. And there before us, only yards away, the whole White Nile thundered 140 feet down through a gap little more than twenty feet wide. That image is still vivid in my mind.

Other occasions that live in my memory include hiring a minibus and driver in Addis Ababa and taking an entire VC10 crew to the Blue Nile gorge, second only in size to the Grand Canyon; taking the train from Lusaka and staying in the Victoria Falls Hotel right on the edge of the falls; going down a gold mine near Johannesburg to a depth of around 6,000 feet (well below sea level); walking through an African village on the banks of Lake Malawi at dawn (I was still on the wrong time zone and couldn't sleep) and being greeted by happy villagers who must have been very surprised to see a lone white man passing by.

I remember one day early on in my career the aircraft went sick in Kano (even VC10s did that sometimes), forcing us to stay until the spares arrived. It was a real lesson in how to handle a problem, one that I tried to emulate later in my career. The captain and station manager organised hotels and hired buses for us all (passengers and crew) to tour around the old city. In 1965, Kano was like something out of *Beau Geste*, with aircraft being greeted on landing by robed men on camels blowing long trumpets! At the end of our enforced stay, one of the passengers remarked that he had never really wanted to be delayed in Kano but was surprised to have enjoyed it so much. I could go on and on...

But there were darker sides too. Like the several days we spent at the Ikeja Arms hotel in Lagos with no power or telephones while rumours of riots ran rife. This was shortly after the massacres in the Congo and, in circumstances like these, the imagination runs away so easily. Or the time we were being driven to Lagos airport in the crew bus during the Biafran War and we came to a road block with soldiers armed with rifles and machine guns; the driver didn't stop at the barrier but accelerated through, and all we crew members threw ourselves under the seats! But nothing happened. However, it was the only time I saw a black African go white with fear! On another occasion, we had to unload the aircraft at gunpoint in Tripoli while Algerian Air Force fighters refuelled on their way to Cairo to support the Egyptians in the Six Day War. No one would refuel our aircraft or unload the holds and when we started to do it ourselves, the army stopped us by surrounding the aircraft. Eventually, after a lot of shouting and arguing, we unloaded everything onto the tarmac, threw the joining passengers' luggage into the holds and departed. The fastest start, taxi and take-off that I can remember — just in case they changed their minds.

Some of the flying problems were interesting too. Early morning arrivals at Nairobi often encountered low cloud which,

At Kano Airport in the 1950s and 1960s the Emir's trumpeter
greeted arriving passengers.

before the days of autoland, meant holding before the cloud lifted. On some occasions, it was necessary to have to work out how best to make the approach with a mixture of navigation aids that were only partly working. Or when we arrived in Lagos to find that half the runway lights were unserviceable because the locals had stolen the copper wires to make bangles. And the time we were taxiing out at Entebbe for a heavy weight departure for London with a growing feeling that something was wrong until it dawned on us that the grass was leaning the wrong way. We stopped on the taxiway and, after a long 'discussion' with the tower, got them to admit that the anemometer had been broken for several days and the wind data they had given us was three days old. So we each made an assessment of the wind speed and direction by looking at the grass, re-did the take-off calculations using our combined estimates, and took off in the opposite direction to ensure we had a head wind!

I have often been asked which was my favourite route. To me, the best was a ten-day triangular trip that could be done in either direction with different selections of stops. For example, the first leg might be to Bahrain, the next to Bombay or Calcutta, as they were then called. Then to Singapore and Hong Kong; back via Singapore and Colombo; then across to the Seychelles and on to either Blantyre or Johannesburg. And finally back to London via Nairobi or Entebbe with night stops all along the way. What a diverse selection of cultures and aeronautical problems; the monsoon in India, the Cheung Chau ADF (automatic direction finding) approach through the harbour to Hong Kong; back to Colombo flying along beside the awe-inspiring thunderstorms of the ITCZ (Intertropical Convergence Zone), filled with sheets of almost continuous lightning. The VOR let down — on limits — to the Seychelles, which involved flying overhead the VOR, heading southeast out to sea, descending to break cloud and then turning back towards the island, (all the while peering through low cloud and driving rain trying to see the lighthouse at Victoria) and then flying along the coast until the approach lights of the

A BOAC Super VC10, G-ASGC, is preserved at Duxford.

airport appeared from behind the hill. All good 'mark one eyeball' stuff.

Then on to Africa for a landing at Blantyre where the narrower than normal runway made it difficult to judge the flare height — the locals used to come out specially to watch the resulting spectacular bounces. Or, alternatively, to Johannesburg with an elevation of 5,500 feet.

What a wonderful trip, and with time off at most of the stops to explore. Rose-tinted spectacles? Yes, most certainly — but that is what memories are made of. What a magnificent aircraft and what wonderfully diverse routes for us to enjoy!

Sweating Blood

'**B**ermuda, Bermuda, Speedbird 312.'

'Speedbird 312, go ahead,' replied Bermuda ATC.

'Bermuda, Speedbird 312, climbing through level 170. We have thunderstorms ahead lying right across our track. Can't see any gaps, can't climb above them, we'll have to deviate well south of track. We need to turn onto heading 240.'

'OK Speedbird, there're no other aircraft in the vicinity. You're clear to deviate south as far as necessary. Report when able to resume course.'

Our Britannia turboprop was flying empty — no passengers, only the crew on board. We had left Bermuda well before dawn, and were climbing on our way west towards Richmond in Virginia to pick up a group of American tourists who had chartered the aircraft for a holiday in Bermuda. No one had told them Bermuda was not a sunny Caribbean island and was due to receive a deluge in a few hours' time!

On the Met forecast at flight briefing, we had seen the front lying across our intended track and had discussed how best to fly round it. A deepening low had left New York and was moving out into the Atlantic. A vigorous cold front stretched down nearly as far as The Bahamas. The thunder tops were reported to be well above 35,000 feet. There was no way a Britannia, designed in the late 1940s and which first flew in 1952, could climb that high; we would have to set off and see if there was a way round.

Passing 18,000 feet, the captain turned towards the south and settled the aircraft onto its new heading. 'What's the heading now skipper?' I asked.

'230. We'll stay on that for a while, I'll tell you when we change.' He went back to the radar searching for a gap in the massive wall of clouds ahead.

The stars had long gone, obscured by high clouds above. Great ribbons of lightning darted between the cloud tops ominously close on our right. Some, lit from within, glowed brown. Purple flashes struck bright down to the sea, others wriggled and writhed in jagged lines along the whole front as far as we could see. 'The brown ones are the worst,' muttered the flight engineer. 'You should see 'em over India in the monsoon.' If they were as bad as this, I shuddered at the thought.

Outside, it was blacker than black, except when bright flashes lit great castles in the sky. Inside, the cockpit lights were turned down to a red glow so the two pilots could see out to correlate what they saw on the weather radar with clouds intermittently lit by lightning.

This was my first flight as a new navigator fresh out of training; I was by far the youngest member of the crew. The last thing I wanted were any complications. I sat at the nav table in the rear right-hand side of the cockpit and plotted the new heading on the chart.

We were now well out of range of the radio beacons on Bermuda, and the stars were hidden by cloud too thick to use the sextant for an astro fix. I would have to rely on Loran, an old wartime long-range radio navigation system.

In its day, Loran was a good navigation aid. Radio stations on the ground, many miles apart, broadcast simultaneous radio pulses. Those from the nearer station were received slightly before those from its pair further away. The navigator then used his receiver to line up the relevant blips on an oscilloscope to measure the time difference between the two pulses. Lines of constant time difference are shown as hyperbolae on the navigation chart and used to fix the position.

All very fine — if clear signals are received. But when I switched on the receiver, instead of two or three simple green 'blips', there were so many rushing across the screen leaving green trails behind them that I couldn't distinguish one from

A BOAC Bristol Britannia 312 at New York (Bob Parrick).

another. Unable to fix our position, I needed to keep an air plot instead. For this, each change of course and true air speed is plotted as a line on the chart, then the wind velocity is applied to derive a DR (dead reckoning) position.

'Heading now 210,' called the captain. I noted the time and plotted it on the chart.

'There's a gap at two o'clock,' said the co-pilot.

The captain checked the radar. 'OK, let's take a look. Turning onto 260.' I plotted the new heading.

'Bugger, that's no use, look at that storm cell beyond the gap. Back on 210,' he said. Again, I plotted the new heading.

We clipped the edge of some cloud — the aircraft began to bump around. Still no fix from the Loran.

'New heading 200,' came from up front. 'No. Now going back onto 230.'

The turbulence increased, my dividers and protractor bounced around the chart table.

The flight deck of a Bristol Britannia.

'Look, there's another gap,' exclaimed the captain, 'we'll try 280.' An eerie purple glow began to spread across the windscreen — St Elmo's fire.

A deafening flash and a crash — all our hearts leapt. We had been struck by lightning. We checked the compasses — good, they still agreed. The turbulence got worse, hail clattered against the windscreen, more lightning lit solid walls of cloud ahead.

'We'll have to get out of here, turning back onto 220.'

The hail stopped. My chart and navigation instruments escaped to the floor. In all the bumps and lurches, it was impossible to plot the courses; all I could do was tighten my seat harness and keep a note so I could plot them later. The engine note changed, we levelled out (if one could call it that) at 24,000 feet but it was more like a roller coaster. I felt vaguely sick.

Another half an hour or so went by as we endured more bumps and lurches and changes of heading, then the captain turned again towards the banks of clouds. 'Heading 270.'

Another huge flash and a crash, a rattle of hail hitting the windscreen, more heaves and bumps, and we were through. Clear air ahead, the horizon just emerging in the gentle grey light of dawn, and — oh bliss — smooth air at last. Now I could try to make sense of all our zigs and zags.

When I was finally done, my plot showed us to be at least 200 miles south of the track to Norfolk on the coast of Virginia. But I couldn't be sure. Had I managed to record all those changes of heading? Had the pilots flown each of them accurately? Had unexpected winds around the thunderstorms blown us even further off course? We could be anywhere within a 100-mile circle. I gave a course to steer to the captain — based on my best guess.

Multiple green blips were still rushing across the Loran screen; I could not line any of them up. Lingering traces of nausea gave way to a different kind of sick feeling in the pit of my stomach. I could make neither head nor tail of the Loran, lingering cloud still hid the stars preventing me from using the sextant, and we were far from any land-based radio beacons. In desperation, I continued to struggle with the Loran. I had little idea of our real position. Sweat trickled down my face.

And yet another problem lay ahead — the ADIZ, the Air Defence Identification Zone. This was 1963, not long after the Cuban Missile Crisis. Any aircraft failing to report the intended time and position for penetrating the ADIZ would be intercepted by US Air Force fighters and the airline fined for non-compliance.

But where were we? I knew we were way off course. I knew the ADIZ was somewhere ahead, but I had no idea how far. Oh God! Another problem. More sweat trickled down my face as I struggled with the infernal Loran.

What would the captain, old enough to be my father, say when I told him I was 'uncertain of our position', a euphemism for being lost! With the ADIZ drawing closer, I decided it was time to tell him.

'Don't worry, lad,' he replied. He was a kindly man who had no doubt been very much more worried many times over wartime

Germany. 'We'll tell 'em we're not too not sure of our position. Give me your best guess and when we get within range of the coastal beacons, we'll give them our exact position. After all that bouncing around, I think we have a pretty good excuse!'

And so we did. Air Traffic Control accepted it without comment. Soon, I managed to get a good fix. I passed an accurate position to the co-pilot who passed it on to ATC, and I began to relax a little. The US Air Force — thankfully — did not come up to intercept us. Instead, the land ahead, bright in the morning sun, welcomed us towards a peaceful haven. After the adrenalin rush of the storm and then being 'uncertain of our position', the relief was intense; the contrast vivid.

We crossed the coast at Norfolk and turned towards Richmond. Descending through a tranquil morning sky to pick up our passengers, the engineer said, 'I bet the punters are going to enjoy the ride through that back to Bermuda.'

'And all the rain they get when the front goes through,' added the co-pilot.

Two weeks later, back in the UK, I was summoned to the Chief Navigator's office in London to explain myself. Fortunately, the company did not have to pay a fine to the US government, but my chart — such as it was — was thoroughly examined.

'Loran is always rather difficult at dawn,' the Chief said. 'Other navigators also reported bad reception that day.'

That was better than I'd expected.

'That's a lesson you won't forget... and it won't be the last time you'll sweat blood at the nav table!'

And it wasn't.

Jumbo Mason

A shadow fell over my face, blocking the warm sun and the light on my book. Pete grinned down at me, 'Thought I'd find you here.'

'Be a dear and rub some of this onto my back.' I rolled over, passed him the tube of sun cream and pointed to the bit I couldn't reach. He sat on the edge of my sunlounger and began to rub.

'Mmmm — lovely.'

'Can I do the front too?'

'No, certainly not! Really — you men are all the same. Why don't you go and get me a nice cold drink instead? Fresh lemonade would be good.'

He sauntered off towards the beach bar. I'd always fancied Pete. He was the first officer on our crew, newly married and, now, definitely off limits. We had been good friends for several years, flirted a bit, gone out together, and enjoyed cosy dinners when we met down the routes. But he had fallen for my flatmate, Judy, instead. I had been her bridesmaid.

Pete was tall, rather diffident, but good fun when you got to know him. In his early thirties, he had a round face and floppy blond hair which fell endearingly across his forehead — very English. Judy was short, bouncy, dark haired and very Irish. The only thing they seemed to have in common was their blue eyes, but it was a fact that they suited each other very well.

He returned with my lemonade and a beer for himself. 'Here you are, Suze, wrap yourself round this.'

'I do wish you wouldn't call me that. You know how much I hate it, sounds like that weird French drink.'

He draped himself over the chair beside me and shot me one of his most charming smiles. When he did that, I could forgive him anything. I wished I'd encouraged him more when we'd been going out together.

'Who's that over there?' I asked, changing the subject. I pointed to two men readying a small sail boat at the water's edge. 'I saw you in the bar with him last night.'

'Which one?'

'The short one. He's climbing in now.'

'Oh, that's Jumbo Mason.'

'Anyone less like an elephant I've yet to meet. Why's he called Jumbo?' I had in mind one of our senior captains — a lovely man, larger than life in every way. Much overweight, he overflowed everything he sat on, including the pilot's seat. But he was well liked and respected by all who flew with him.

'It all started when he met an elephant on an aeroplane,' Pete said.

'Come off it. Is this another of your tall stories?'

'No, it's absolutely true. He really did meet an elephant. In fact, he spent several hours talking to it.'

I looked across at Jumbo who was now steering out towards the open water. He had the lean looks of an athlete and obviously knew how to handle a boat. I was intrigued. When I'd seen him in the bar with Pete, I'd noticed how neat he looked — sharp features, carefully brushed hair, pale blue long-sleeved shirt, perfectly creased fawn slacks and matching espadrilles. It was clear he took trouble over his appearance.

'It was some while ago, when he was still a first officer.'

'Do you mean he's a captain now? He looks far too young.' I was even more intrigued. 'What's he like?'

'Bit of a stickler, more so since he got his command. You'll see what I mean when you fly with him tomorrow. Anyway, he met his elephant somewhere between Delhi and Teheran.'

'You're kidding.'

'No, I'm not.'

'Surely it was in the hold.'

'Yes — and that's the whole point. It all started as a mystery.

They were cruising along very nicely when suddenly the aeroplane gave a slight lurch. Nothing in particular, but it made them look around, checking all the instruments. Everything looked normal. The autopilot was doing what it should. The engines were OK. And that was that for a while. Then there was another lurch. Jumbo said it was "like driving over a sleeping policeman rather too fast.'"

'What's his real name?'

'John. But everyone calls him Jumbo these days.'

Pete explained that before all the automatic navigation gubbins they use nowadays, they flew with a four-man crew: captain, two first officers — one co-piloting, the other navigating — and a flight engineer. On this leg of the journey, it was Jumbo's turn to navigate, which didn't amount to much on airways over Pakistan, all he had to do was look after the paperwork. So the captain asked him to go back to see if the cabin crew had noticed anything odd.

'Jumbo reported they'd felt the lurch but nothing untoward. They were busy and about to start the meal service. You know better than me what it's like, preparing the trolleys, passengers getting in the way making a last-minute dash to the loo.'

I knew only too well. I had been a stewardess in first class for two years now and it was always a rush to get everything ready. Hot towels, canapés, silver service, choice of main course, dessert, cheese, fine wines and coffee. On BOAC, they expected the best, and we gave it to them.

'Jumbo returned to the nav table. The stewardess brought up

a pot of tea and asked him to do the honours while they were serving the punters. At that point the aircraft gave an even bigger lurch, spilling the tea all over the paperwork. Jumbo didn't like that. It spoilt his neat log and chart. Then the chief steward came up to say he'd heard crunching sounds from beneath the floor.'

As I listened, I watched Jumbo reappear around the headland and sail back fast towards the shore. He approached the beach, turned slightly into wind, ran the boat up onto the sand and stepped neatly ashore without even wetting his feet. His friend joined him and, together, they turned the boat round so the other man could sail out into the bay. Jumbo watched for a while, walked up the beach and went to sit in the shade of a coconut palm. He reached under his chair, put on his sunglasses and opened his book.

'You're not listening, Susan.'

'Yes I am. There were crunching noises.'

A Boeing 707 (foreground) and five VC10s at BOAC's London Heathrow maintenance base.

'The captain didn't like the sound of that. So the flight engineer went into the cabin to see if he could hear anything, but all was well, and they continued serenely on their way.'

'You might think it serene, but it's not for us. All you lot do up front in the cockpit is gaze out of the window and demand endless cups of tea. Try doing a full meal service on a short sector for a change.'

'It might surprise you to know that we do twiddle a few knobs and tits from time to time. I've even been known to look at the odd instrument.'

I gave him one of my more severe looks and he went on to describe what happened next. The aircraft had made several more lurches, more severe than before. The flight engineer went into the cabin again and, this time, he too heard ominous noises. He'd knelt down and put his ear to the floor of the aisle in first class. He returned to the flight deck looking distinctly worried and asked to see the loadsheet. The noises were definitely coming from the forward freight bay. He wanted to know where the ruddy elephant was stowed.

'We carry a lot of animals.' Pete continued, 'Dogs, cats, monkeys, snakes, parrots, tropical fish and, on this occasion, a baby elephant going to the London zoo. It had been loaded in Delhi, and was quite small.'

'Poor little thing. Isn't it cold down there?'

'No. The air's the same as the cabin. Temperature's much the same.'

The captain and the flight engineer examined the loadsheet and confirmed that the elephant was indeed in the forward hold, roughly where the noises were coming from. The engineer thought he'd better take a look. Pete explained that below the nav table at the back of the flight deck on the 707, there was a small trapdoor in the floor through which access could be gained to the electrics bay. At the aft end of this there was another trapdoor through which it was just possible to squeeze into the forward freight compartment. The engineer disappeared below and after much effing and blinding re-emerged to say the elephant had broken out of its crate. It had climbed onto

25

some suitcases and was pressing its back against the ceiling. And it was very upset.

'Wouldn't you be? Poor little soul,' I exclaimed. 'All alone in the dark, lost his mummy, nasty noises — and being shaken all around. I'd be upset too.'

'It was much more serious than that. Every time he stood up and pressed against the ceiling, he was pressing against the control cables.'

I could see this might be a problem and Pete explained just how vital they were. They ran on pulleys along the ceiling of the freight bay immediately under the cabin floor. They connected the pilots' controls to the elevators on the tail and were only protected by some thin fibreglass shielding. Each time the elephant pressed against the cables they moved the elevators, making the aircraft pitch up and down. What if one of the cables broke? They might not be able to control the aircraft. And a safe landing would be very difficult — perhaps even impossible.

'So what did they do?'

'The flight engineer asked what elephants eat. The chief steward, who'd come up to report even more strange noises said fruit and veg. The captain asked what they had on board and whether they'd served lunch yet. The chief steward said they hadn't. There were green beans with the main course and tropical fruit salad for dessert. Also, the salad bowls hadn't been dressed yet.'

So they made a plan. The captain used the PA to explain the problem to the passengers. The chief steward organised the cabin crew to strip all the fruit and veg from the passengers' meals. A chain gang was formed to pass it up to the flight deck. Poor old Jumbo was detailed to go down into the freight bay to feed the elephant.

'Jumbo was not amused. You saw how nattily he dresses. His uniforms are ultra-neat too. I don't know whether you've ever looked into the holds. They're dirty at the best of times, only about four feet of headroom. Jumbo had to squeeze past suitcases and other odds and ends to reach the elephant. He

First class cabin service on a BOAC VC10.

then had to crouch down in the cramped space between the baggage and try to keep it calm.'

'How did they pass the food down to him?'

'The smallest steward climbed into the electrics bay and was told, on pain of death, not to touch anything — all the radios and other electrical things are in there. One of the stewardesses lay on the floor below the nav table, passing down the various delicacies that elephants were thought to fancy. It all worked quite well until the elephant tried to run around. Jumbo had to rugger tackle it. I gather it got quite fraught, and you know what happens when animals get frightened.'

I did. I told Pete I wasn't a farmer's daughter for nothing. As a child, I had helped with the milking and mucking out. I had seen the damage when one of our cows had broken through the fence into our garden. It had taken a long time to coax her out. The resulting mess had been spectacular.

'It was much the same for Jumbo. The elephant liked the bananas and mangos but, to coin a phrase, it turned its trunk up at the lettuce. It expressed its displeasure by depositing a very large poo. The steward in the electrics bay told everyone afterwards that Jumbo had slipped and sat in it.'

I couldn't help laughing. 'It sounds even worse than being a galley slave.'

'They were down there well over an hour before landing in Teheran. Most of the time Jumbo'd been able to feed it and cuddle it to keep it quiet. But when the elephant tried to escape, they'd rolled around together in a combination of trampled fruit and elephant excrement. When Jumbo was finally extricated, he smelt to high heaven — and looked like shit.'

Seeing Jumbo quietly reading his book in the shade of the palm tree, I felt a pang of sympathy. It couldn't have been easy placating a frightened elephant in such a tiny space, although I was sure the story had been much exaggerated. 'Hard to imagine now,' I said.

'Exactly. And he was acutely embarrassed when he'd had to walk past the passengers queuing at immigration in the terminal building. Some of them knew what he'd done and thanked him. Others held their noses, pointed at his trousers and sniggered.'

'And at the hotel?' I asked.

'He disappeared up to his room double quick. But word soon got around. In the bar that night, one of the stewards called him Jumbo and asked when was feeding time at the zoo?'

'What cheek.'

'They found it all the funnier because he's always so fastidious. You're flying with him tomorrow. I'll introduce you to him if you like, but for heaven's sake don't call him "Jumbo".'

'Oh. He's not one of those who always wants to be called "Sir" is he?'

'No. Just doesn't like Jumbo or being asked about zoos.'

'That's OK. I'll butter him up and call him "Daaaahling" instead.'

'I believe you will too.'

There's More to Flying than That!

Hamish Reid came from a seafaring family in Dundee. Rather than follow his elder brother into the navy, he joined the RAF when he was barely nineteen and, after training, was posted to a Lancaster squadron in Lincolnshire. That was in January 1944, a year before the end of the war.

He had been fortunate. Merely surviving the thirty raids of his one and only tour of duty required a fair amount of skill and a huge dose of luck. Half of all Bomber Command aircrew were lost before they completed ten missions. Such losses had left him deeply fatalistic, with a tough, no-nonsense attitude to life. After the war, like many of his colleagues, he found it difficult to return to normal life.

Demobilisation left him drifting aimlessly. He was not academically inclined. Had the war not intervened, he would probably have finished the engineering apprenticeship he had begun on leaving school. He tried working in a garage but found it boring. Despite the horrors in the night skies over Germany, he enjoyed the craft of flying. Its precision, its discipline, the sense of achievement appealed to his self-reliant practical nature. Besides, there was little else he was trained to do. So when he saw an advert asking for pilots to join BOAC, he applied immediately and soon found himself flying Avro Yorks, a transport version of the Lancaster bomber he had flown in the war.

Now, some 25 years later, halfway between Bahrain and Colombo, far out over the Arabian Sea, in the blackness of the night, he contemplated the wall of thunderstorms ahead. Lit by continuous ribbons of lightning, they lay ominously across his path. Magnificent but deadly, he knew they hid real dangers

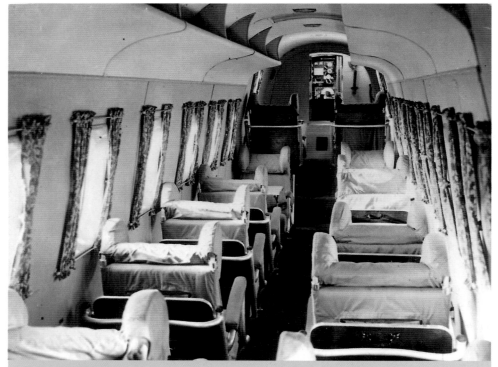

The Avro York, based on the Lancaster bomber, was used extensively by BOAC in the years following the Second World War.

within — hail, ice and vicious turbulence. Many times he had fought his way through in noisy piston-engine aircraft, the ice rattling off the propellers against the fuselage. Before the days of weather radar, it was very much a hit-and-miss affair, uncomfortable and sometimes hazardous. Here, in the roomy cockpit of a VC10, Britain's latest jet airliner, flying serenely above the weather, he fully expected to pass these storms with ease. But — Christ, these buggers are high, he thought. I'm at 35,000 feet and still they tower above me.

On the weather radar by his left knee, he searched for gaps in the line stretching continuously from east to west across the screen. He turned down the cockpit lights, telling young Jim in the co-pilot's seat to do the same so they could look out and correlate what they saw on the radar with the cloud tops ahead.

Hamish was deeply suspicious of the abilities of these new pilots straight from civil flying school. He had little faith in those who had not learnt to fly the hard way. How well would they manage in real emergencies? He had survived many, but this young boy beside him... ? He bristled behind his moustache at the very idea of the company even letting them fly jets. Unbloodied by war, what did they know about flying?

He much preferred seasoned ex-military men. Take Graham Poole for example, his senior co-pilot, ex-air force, hadn't seen combat, yet the product of a disciplined, rigorous training. Chris Carter, the flight engineer, the same; both men with nearly as much flying experience as himself. But Jim? Nice enough, fresh out of training, keen, eager, but still wet behind the ears.

As for Jim, he knew of the captain's reputation. Even before they met in the crew briefing room in London, he worried his inexperience would show. He felt so excluded. The three senior men had joked about things of which he knew little. No one was unkind exactly, but neither did they encourage him to join in their camaraderie. It would be a long trip out to Hong Kong and back. How would he fit in? Would the captain allow him to fly a sector? Or would he have to navigate and be the crew dogsbody? In the event, the captain had flown the first sector to Beirut, Graham the second to Bahrain, and now it was his turn while Graham navigated. He hoped he would do alright.

Despite his doubts, Hamish was pleasantly surprised at how well Jim flew the aircraft. But the real test lay ahead. Somehow, they had to find a way around these storms — he'd never seen them so high. He wondered what the lad would decide.

'New heading 120,' Graham advised, interrupting Hamish's train of thought. Jim turned a few degrees left to settle on the new course.

Hamish again checked the radar. He waited for Jim to say something. Can't stay on this course for long, there's a dangerous-looking storm cell almost straight ahead. 'Well, laddie — which way do you want to turn?' Jim hesitated and suggested returning to their original course, or perhaps a little further to the right.

'What about that even bigger one just beyond it?' The lad looked puzzled. 'Better go due east for a while and look for a wider gap.'

Jim was relieved the captain had made the decision for him. He knew about thunderstorms, he'd seen them in Europe, read about them in text books, and it had been drilled into him during training to avoid them by at least 20 miles. But this was the monsoon in India — he'd never seen anything like it.

They paralleled the storm clouds for 50 miles, hoping for a gap. When one appeared, Hamish waited for the lad to do something. 'Try that one, make it 170.' Jim did as suggested, turning the aircraft south onto a heading of 170 degrees.

Hamish called the chief steward and told him to secure the cabin. 'Could be a rough ride, get all the cabin crew strapped in too.' And he switched on the fasten seat belt signs. They were creeping now between towering walls of cloud, glowing brown and purple in the dark. Savage bolts of lightning danced between, around and below them. Light turbulence began to rock the aircraft.

'Everyone turn the cockpit lights up bright, we don't want to be blinded.' This was for the young lad's edification. St Elmo's fire darted, flickering purple tentacles across the windscreen. A strong ozone electrical smell permeated the cockpit. He told Jim to turn more to starboard to thread a way into another gap. 'But make sure you stay well clear of that bugger out on the right.'

Radio static sizzled in their headsets. Ice particles twinkled past the cockpit windows. The turbulence grew heavier. Another dog-leg, then — WUMPH! A huge bolt of lightning struck just below the cockpit window on the co-pilot's side. Shocked, blinded and deafened, Jim wondered for a moment if he was still alive.

The electrical smell grew worse. Hamish shouted, 'Bloody hell!' A pause. 'What's happened to the radar? Anything on

While not a hazard in itself, St Elmo's fire is an indication of storm activity and may be a precursor to a lightning strike. Pictured: the flight deck of a Boeing 777.

yours?' He looked across to Jim's side. Both screens were blank. 'Shit! No radar, can't go through that lot with no radar.' The lad went white, transfixed in his seat.

'I have control. Turning left. There's more room this side.' Hamish disconnected the autopilot and banked round sharply to reverse the heading. They clipped some cloud, the aircraft shuddered, hail rattled against the windscreen. Strange vibrations from somewhere near the nose began to shake the cockpit, blurring the flight instruments. With no radar, semi-blinded by lightning, Hamish tried to remember the headings he needed to retrace their path back between the clouds.

KERUMPH! They were struck again. Hamish pulled the aircraft round even harder. Jim came alive. Horrified. Why was the captain standing it on its wing tip? 'Bank,' he shouted, 'Bank!' warning Hamish he had banked over too far. Hamish levelled the wings. What was the lad so scared about? He made another dog-leg onto a heading of 350 to clear a cloud full of lightning — but something was wrong. Heavy lurches threw them violently against their straps. More hail crashed against the windscreen and the vibration increased. And the noise too.

Then they were out in the clear. Hamish re-engaged the autopilot. His heart thumping, cold sweat ran down his spine. He turned down the cockpit lights and pressed his face against the side window. Stars. Thank God, no more thunderclouds, only a spread of white stratus way below, lit by the moon. Better not say anything about that moment.

'Sir,' shouted Jim above the din, 'compass comparator light's on. My compass is reading 310, what's yours?'

'350 my side.'

'That checks,' Chris leant forward between them. 'Yours is the one that's out, Captain, the standby shows 310 too.'

Hamish knew the little E2B standby compass was of limited use, he wanted a better check. 'Graham,' he shouted, 'can you check 'em by astro?'

'I'll need a few minutes. Is it clear above?'

'Yes. I can just see the Pole Star out to the right, it's pretty low on the horizon.'

Graham went to work with the Air Almanac to calculate the star's true direction so that he could use the sextant to check the compasses. But the noise and vibration made it hard to concentrate, and some of his nav equipment was scattered around the cockpit floor.

'Airspeed's up the spout too. Look at the speed on Jim's side, it's far too low. Yours is OK, Captain. It agrees with my ASI back here,' shouted Chris. 'It's Jim's that's wrong.'

Hamish thought for a moment. 'I'll use my side for speed and Jim's for heading. Graham, how are you doing with that astro check?'

'Coming, sir, not much longer.' A few minutes later, Graham tapped Hamish on the shoulder and shouted into his ear. 'Jim's compass is accurate. I'll give you a course to steer as soon as I've finished this fix.'

Hamish now had enough to work with, but the vibration and noise worried him. It was getting worse. And why was the lad so frightened about him making a steep turn? He'd only banked over to 60 degrees, still safe in his opinion.

Jim was more composed now. Yes, the lightning bolt had startled him, he was looking out of the window when it had struck only feet below his nose. He'd been blinded. Why had the captain nearly rolled the aircraft upside down? What did he think he was doing? So he'd shouted. The captain was not pleased.

'Captain,' Graham came forward between the two pilots, spreading the chart on the centre console so they could see where he was pointing. 'I've got a fix, we're here. Bombay's our nearest diversion airfield. Up here, just over 400 miles away. I've checked the weather, it's clear. 050 would be a good course for now. I'll give you something better in a moment.'

'Chris,' Hamish leant back and tugged at Chris's sleeve, 'how much fuel do we have?'

'Just over 20 tonnes, Captain.'

'That gives us nearly four hours. More than enough if you decide to divert.' Graham put down his Dalton computer and awaited the captain's decision.

'Right, we'll go to Bombay.' And he told Jim to call Bombay on the HF radio. 'Tell 'em we've been struck by lightning, radar's U/S, ETA Bombay is 22.15.' Jim made attempt after attempt, but with so much static interference on the radio he couldn't hear any reply. No one seemed to be listening. And the noise from outside was like a hundred express trains thundering by. The vibration didn't help either.

A loud bang shook the airframe, the vibration increased and so did the noise. Hamish's thoughts flew back to 1944 when he'd nursed a badly damaged Lancaster back to base. Hit by flak. Huge explosion. Hole in the side. Flight engineer badly injured. Losing fuel. Would they need to ditch in the North Sea? Got home — just. After landing, they found even more holes in the wings. They were lucky nothing caught fire.

Suddenly, his airspeed went haywire. This was now — not back then. Christ, what a mess! Chris leant forward with the Flying Manual. 'The good book says we can make a standby selection to the number three pitot. That way we'll have good readings on all three ASIs, but only from one source. Not ideal, but better than what we have now.' Chris shouted out the selections required: 'Captain's selector switch "down", co-pilot's "up", and the standby selector switch to the "down"'position.' They compared readings. It all looked OK.

Hamish considered his options. The lad had flown the aircraft quite well, no doubt he'd been shocked by the lightning strike, but why was he so reluctant to make decisions? Now, with unreliable flight instruments, Hamish wanted the more experienced pilot at the controls beside him. He would wait until they were within range of the radio beacons on the coast when Graham no longer needed to navigate. Then he would change them round. But what of his own reaction? He hadn't

In 1968, a BOAC VC10 was severely damaged by hail. With help from an RAF Hunter, the aircraft landed safely at Bahrain. Note the missing radome in this MOD photograph.

banked so far. From the depths of his mind had come this urgent need to turn, to twist, to dive. To avoid the foe, the flak, the fighter. He'd only just resisted the urge to dive. Was it still so deeply ingrained?

He'd nearly made a grave mistake. He knew it in his heart, but he wouldn't admit it, and certainly not to the others. Damn it, I must be getting old.

Jim stared straight ahead. What had the captain been thinking? Why stand the aircraft on its wingtip? Was he crazy? Stupid old bugger, perhaps he was past it.

Behind them, at the nav table, Graham was quite impressed — Jim had been right to shout. Chris, at the engineer's station, buried himself in the manuals trying to figure out what might be damaged. Funny blokes pilots, good thing they had flight engineers to keep an eye on 'em — he'd been about to shout 'bank' too. He was pretty sure the fibreglass radome that covered the radar scanner in the nose had been struck by the lightning. Maybe some of it had broken away.

Chris explained his conclusions to Hamish who only grunted. Sod him, thought Chris. Try to help him and that's all the thanks you get. Also, why hadn't Hamish said something to the passengers? He wondered whether to suggest something, but turned to Graham instead. Together, they checked their figures — groundspeed, distance, time to Bombay, fuel consumption, fuel remaining on arrival. 'We may need to dump some fuel before landing, Captain,' Chris said. Hamish grunted again.

'Sir,' Jim hesitated, 'I've got through to Bombay at last. Would you like me to ask them to advise company we're diverting?'

'Yes, and when you've done that, I want Graham in that seat.' Not a word of explanation.

'Don't take it too hard,' Graham said as they changed over.

Jim felt useless. He sat at the nav table at the back of the cockpit, looking through Graham's navigation calculations. But the noise, the noise, the noise. Worse than express trains, more like a howling hurricane, it rattled your teeth, bounced your eyeballs, entered your brain, and blotted out rational thought. He turned to Chris and asked what the hell he thought was happening. Chris thought it probably came from the disrupted airflow round the nose cone. That would also explain why the Airspeed Indicators (ASIs) were not reading correctly. Well, they'd know soon enough when they landed in Bombay, but it was unusual for modern compasses to be affected by lightning. He showed Jim the system diagrams in the technical manual which explained how each compass derived its magnetic heading from independent fluxgates in the wingtips. Perhaps the right wingtip had been struck by lightning too.

'Can I see the Cruise Control Manual?' Jim asked. He studied the maze of lines on the graphs for a while. 'Look, if we descended, we could slow up and maybe reduce this bloody noise. What do you think?'

'Worth a try. Suggest it to the boss.'

Jim went forward to where Hamish sat hunched, still and silent at the controls. 'Captain,' he shouted above the din, showing him the graph. 'If we descended early, we could slow up to reduce the noise.' He explained they could then experiment to find a speed that gave the least noise.

Only good idea the lad has had all night, thought Hamish. He leant across to Graham and told him to call Bombay to see if they could get a lower level. Bombay confirmed there was no other traffic, they could experiment as necessary.

Down at 19,000 feet, Hamish found the slower speed much better. The vibration reduced, and the noise too. Not long to go now. At least we have lots of fuel and the aircraft is responding well to the controls. Thank heavens it's a clear night. Should see the lights on the coast soon. Gradually they came in sight and he began to slow some more. He asked Graham to lower the flaps. That's good, they are working normally. The noise and vibration lessened. He could see the approach lights now. He checked the compass heading with Graham. He turned the aircraft to line up with the runway. They crossed the coast. Nearly home.

Jim watched the approach lights grow closer and slide beneath the nose. Then the outstretched arms of the runway

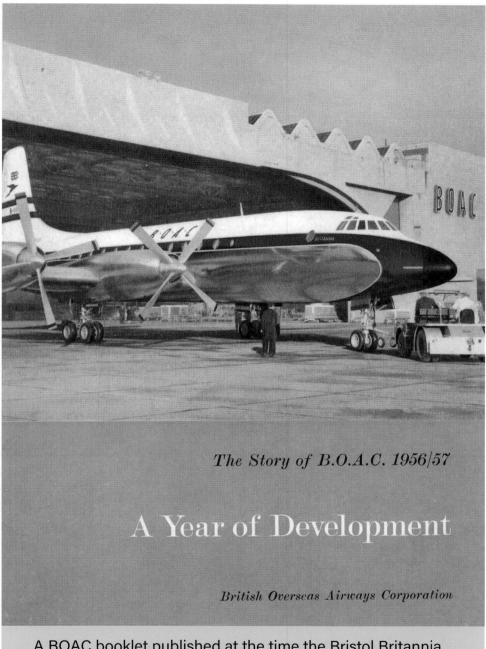

The Story of B.O.A.C. 1956/57

A Year of Development

British Overseas Airways Corporation

A BOAC booklet published at the time the Bristol Britannia entered service.

lights as they rose on either side in a welcoming embrace. Oh! The relief when the aircraft sank gratefully onto the tarmac. The reassuring rumble of wheels, the roar of reverse thrust, and the tug of brakes as Hamish slowed the aircraft and turned off the runway towards the terminal buildings. Quiet at last, they came to a halt. Steps were brought to the forward passenger door, the ground engineer burst into the cockpit, 'What happened? You should see the nose, nothing there, radome's all gone.'

'I think we'll be here for a while,' responded Hamish. 'Are they taking the passengers to hotels?' He started to write up the incident report while Chris went outside to look at the damage.

'Only a few bits of the radome left, scanner's bent, starboard pitot tube's all twisted. No obvious damage that I can see elsewhere. Wings look OK. But they'd better check the engines in the morning,' he reported when he returned.

'Shut-down checks are all complete, I think we're done in here. Let's go and look outside. We'll take the books and finish the reports in the office. We can talk to London too.'

Hamish led the way out of the cockpit. The passengers had gone by the time they descended the steps and gathered under the nose to inspect the damage.

Jim was aghast to see the shattered radome, and said as much to Graham.

'Nay, that's nothing,' observed Hamish in his dry Scottish accent, 'If you haven't been shot at over the Ruhr, laddie, you don't know what flyin's all aboot.' And without another word, he stomped off, followed by Chris, to the office to finish his report.

Graham raised an eyebrow at Jim. 'Don't mind him, there's more to flying than that. He's a crusty old sod at times — a little more humanity would go a long way. Remember — his early experiences were very different from ours. You were right to shout when you did. Let's join the cabin crew in the bus. I expect they're pretty shattered too.'

The Venetian Blind

Senior First Officer Terence Archibald Frederick Flynn was in a particularly good mood. He had just checked the crew list and found that Amanda Berkeley was on the flight. She was an old flame with whom he had spent several enjoyable crew stops in the past. He was looking forward to renewing their liaison.

'Morning, Taff — checking the runners and riders then?'

'Good morning, Willie.'

It was Bill Williams, the flight engineer. They had flown together many times before and, being good friends, had helped each other in and out of various scrapes. Taff felt the omens foretold a fun trip and Bill guessed why.

Despite his Celtic name, Taff was English through and through and, being neither Irish nor Welsh, disliked his nickname. Bill equally disliked having been christened William Williams — there were far too many Williamses where he had come from. Bill was short, round and obviously Welsh, while Taff was tall, fine featured, with unruly dark hair and cool grey eyes. He was a magnet for women — and knew it.

In the briefing room, they found Colin Fraser, the captain, discussing the route with Simon Taylor, the other co-pilot, most of whose flying till now had been on Atlantic routes. This was his first time going east and the trip was scheduled to stop in some interesting places — Beirut, Delhi, and then back via Teheran. He liked Colin's genial understated manner and he, too, felt the omens were good.

Bill, who knew the Middle East and India well, offered to introduce Simon to the many delights along the way, the first being the famed Golden Bar in Beirut. Taff, on the other hand, while perfectly affable, was secretly pleased to observe that

41

Beirut, before the Lebanese Civil War, was known as the 'Paris of The East' and became a popular slip for BOAC crews.
Pictured: La Gondola Restaurant in 1960.

Simon was unlikely to offer any competition so far as the girls were concerned.

The flight to Beirut was routine, the passengers behaved like lambs, giving Amanda plenty of time to think about Taff. She was looking forward to being with him again; she knew his reputation, but loved his company and forgave him his wicked ways. She thought back to when they had first met in Barbados. She was not a forward girl but, on that occasion, had been a willing accomplice. And she had enjoyed their meetings ever since.

Like many BOAC stewardesses in the 1960s, she came from a good family. Her father was a vicar somewhere in the West Country, where she had had a comfortable, if slightly overprotected, childhood. She had been educated at Cheltenham Ladies' College and longed for adventure.

When she had said she was joining BOAC, her father was horrified. During the war, he had been an army padre and had seen too much of the licentious ways of young men. He had tried hard to dissuade his only daughter, but without success. Her mother, having been a nurse, was a good deal more practical, and advised Amanda to take 'precautions'.

When they arrived in Beirut, the crew bus took them to their hotels — the flight crew to The Carlton, the cabin crew to The Bristol. The Carlton looked out over the Corniche towards the incredible blue of the Mediterranean. But The Bristol was in the noisy hubbub of the town centre — and opposite its entrance was the Golden Bar. Despite its name and reputation, it was, in fact, a bit of a dump, set into a row of non-descript buildings. The interior was dingy, dusty and nearly always over-crowded. Behind the bar, which ran down one side, were rows of assorted bottles. At the far end, a jukebox drowned out even the loudest conversation. Nevertheless, it was a popular meeting place for airline crews of many nationalities. They agreed to meet there that evening.

Most of the crew had already gathered when Taff came in. Simon was with Amanda and one of the other girls near the juke-box, trying to find something to play, other than the loud Arabic music enjoyed by the locals. Bill was at the bar, talking to Colin and one of the stewards. 'Watch this,' Bill said. 'Bit of an item they are, see. Simon doesn't have a chance.'

Taff made a beeline for the girls and slid his hand over Amanda's shoulder. She was a striking girl, perhaps not conventionally beautiful, but elegant, poised and with warm beguiling eyes. She was smoking and talking to Vicki, a very attractive red-head who was leaning against the wall, displaying a svelte figure and generous cleavage. Taff looked her over appreciatively as Amanda introduced him. He offered them both another gin and tonic.

'See what I mean, they both fancy 'im. Simon won't get a look-in. Let's go and join 'em.'

Bill pushed his way over, trying not to spill his beer. Simon was clearly enjoying the attention of the girls until Taff rolled up. Other crew members came to join them; it was developing into a good shindig. At some stage quite late on, no one knew when, Taff disappeared. A little later, Bill noticed the two girls had disappeared too, but said nothing. It was late when the party broke up, some went round to a local restaurant, but Colin, Bill and Simon excused themselves, saying they were leaving for Delhi next day.

At breakfast there was no sign of Taff. Bill rolled his eyes. 'Don't know how he does it.' Simon wondered if he was always like this. As the time for pick-up approached, Colin became a little concerned — they could hardly leave for Delhi without their second-in-command. Just in time, Taff appeared looking rather pleased with himself. He sat at the front of the bus on the way to the airport, well away from Amanda, reading his book, and saying nothing.

During the flight to Delhi, Bill waited until Colin had gone back to visit the cabin before asking Taff whether he'd had a good evening. 'Yes,' said Taff but complained about the discomfort of the single rooms in The Bristol.

'Serves you right, boyo. Should've come back with us to The Carlton.'

In Delhi, they all stayed together in the same hotel — one which belonged to a well-known American chain. The building was in two blocks set on either side of a courtyard, and joined by a low section containing the reception area and restaurants. All the rooms had comfortable double beds.

As was the custom, they gathered in Colin's room before going to bed. At three in the morning, after a long night flight, you need a few drinks to wind down before trying to go to sleep at dawn. This room, as befitted the captain, was larger than the others, and situated high up in one of the blocks facing the courtyard.

'Hi there, boys and girls.' Charlie Payne entered with two almost-full bottles of champagne, followed by another steward with a bottle of brandy. 'Tooth mugs at the ready, it's champagne cocktail time.' Charles had served on the Cunard Queens before joining BOAC and knew a thing or two about looking after his colleagues. He was also a close observer of human foibles and a good mimic. They settled around the room, on the bed, in chairs and wherever there was space on the floor. Taff and Amanda were noticeable by their absence.

'Hey, look at this.' Bill was standing by the open curtains, pointing towards a window low down in the opposite block. There, for all to see, and beautifully lit by the bedside lamp, were Taff and Amanda naked on the bed. Unfortunately for them, they had failed to notice that the slats of their venetian blind were tilted up rather than down, affording those high up in the other block an unobstructed view of the proceedings.

'Which room are they in?'

'326,' said Vicki.

'Leave them be,' said Colin.

'No, I've a better idea. Charlie, how good's your God imitation?' Bill waited for *le moment critique*, dialled 326 and handed the phone to Charlie. They all watched as Taff reached across to answer the call.

'This is God speaking. You should be ashamed of yourselves,' thundered Charlie in a deep authoritarian voice.

The effect was as hoped. Amanda pulled the sheets up to cover her nakedness. Taff jumped off the bed much to the audience's delight, but then, to everyone's disappointment, switched off the light.

'Bet they wondered where that came from.'

'In like Flynn' observed Vicki.

'More like "in and out like Flynn",' chuckled Bill.

'Shame to spoil the fun. Show's over. Time for bed, said Zebedee.' The party broke up amid much guffawing and ribald remarks.

'Hope young Errol enjoyed his oats,' added Colin as he closed the door, hoping for some peace and quiet at last.

Taff did not appear that afternoon, and neither did Amanda. Nor were they seen the whole of the next day. Pick up for their next flight to Teheran was at six the following morning.

Surprisingly, Taff and Amanda were down in the foyer in good time. There were a few smirks on the bus to the airport, no one mentioned God.

But someone at the back of the bus called out, 'And how's Errol this morning?'

Colin was secretly pleased he was not young any more.

The Rivals

Sophie Baldwin was quietly drinking a coffee in the foyer of the Panafric Hotel in Nairobi when the northbound crew from Jo'burg came in. She watched the usual huddle around the check-in desk while rooms were allocated and porters brought in the bags. A tall man with tousled hair, sporting the three gold rings of a senior first officer, separated himself from the group and came towards her. Sophie had flown with him before and thought him rather good looking, but, perhaps, a little too full of himself.

Taff removed his dark glasses and beamed a winning smile at her. 'What a surprise to find you here. May I join you while they sort the bags out?'

'How was the flight up?'

'Fine, except for the bloody captain.' And he pointed towards a small round figure disappearing into the lift. 'You'd think he's a country squire with a large estate the way he talks. Grand this, grand that — more like a semi in Surbiton I should think. Four hours with Jimmie is more than enough for one day. What are you doing tonight?'

'We're all meeting at The Thorn Tree. Haven't fixed a time yet. Like to join us?'

'Good idea. I can escape from Jimmie — and we could slope off for *dinner à deux.*' He gave her a meaningful look. 'Give me a buzz when you know the time, room 403. Right now, I'm in urgent need of a siesta.'

Picking up his cap and briefcase, he went over to the check-in desk to collect his key and asked to see the crew list. He made a careful note of Sophie's room number, it might be useful later.

The Thorn Tree Café at the New Stanley Hotel was a popular meeting place for BOAC crews in Nairobi.

Nairobi was a great meeting place for BOAC crews in Africa, some going south like Sophie's crew, others on their way north, returning to London, some doing a shuttle to Dar es Salaam and back, or leaving for a night stop in the Seychelles or Mauritius. There were usually at least two or three complete VC10 crews there at any one time. Taff was looking forward to a whole day off; Sophie would be the icing on the cake.

She decided to go out to the pool and have a lazy afternoon. It was too hot in the sun so she wandered over to sit in the shade under the umbrellas.

Vicki peeped out at her from under a large sunhat as she sat down. 'Hi, coming to join me?' She had red hair and that pale Celtic skin that burns so easily. Sophie was blonde, slim and with a golden tan. Both were extremely good looking. She told Vicki about meeting Taff.

'You want to watch Errol, he has a reputation,' Vicki warned.

'I know, but why d'you call him *Errol*?'

'Haven't you heard? I thought everyone knew about Delhi.'

'No. What happened? Do tell.'

'It was a couple of months ago,' explained Vicki. 'We'd just got in from Beirut, a night flight, then an early morning room party in the skipper's room. You know — champagne cocktails all round, everyone letting their hair down. We noticed Taff hadn't turned up, and neither had Amanda, Amanda Berkeley. D'you know her?'

'The vicar's daughter?'

'Yes, to look at her, butter wouldn't melt in her mouth but she has a very soft spot for Errol, I mean Taff.' And Vicki went on to tell her about how, at the room party, Bill, their flight engineer, had looked out of the window and found he could see down through their venetian blind. 'They were in bed, in a room low down across the courtyard, where we all could see the two of them going at it like rabbits. Charlie Payne thought he'd play a joke. He phoned them and said, "This is God. You should be ashamed of yourselves." You know what a good mimic he is. Well the effect was dramatic. Taff jumped off the bed and Amanda covered herself with a sheet, but not before our whole crew had seen all her charms.'

'What a hoot. But I still don't see why you call him *Errol*.'

'"In like Flynn"? You know — the film star, and when Bill added, "more like in and out like Flynn" we all collapsed. Poor Taff, when he jumped off the bed in confusion something else collapsed as well — very plain to see.'

'Well, I think he's lining me up for a date this evening. He wants to join us, wants to escape from his boring old captain — Jimmie something.'

'You don't sound too keen. But he's good fun, you know.'

'Why don't you ring him up, do you have his room number? Arrange a rendezvous and I'll go instead.'

'Won't he be angry?'

'I doubt it. I'll spin a yarn of some sort and then we'll disappear off to dinner.'

Sophie went over to the pool bar and used their phone to call room 403. She told Taff her crew were meeting at six that evening, why didn't he meet her in the foyer a little before and they could take a taxi together down to The Thorn Tree.

'All fixed?'

'Yes. He sounded very pleased with himself.'

'What'll you say to him when he sees it's you?'

'Tell him you have a headache or something and I fancy having him all to myself. He won't delve any deeper when he sees it's me, he has a thing about cleavage. I'll ask him to take me to that little restaurant on Mama Ngina Street. It's very discreet.'

Sophie decided to go down to The Thorn Tree around four for tea, that way she would avoid Taff in the foyer.

Early next morning they were up at six for an eight o'clock take-off and the four-hour flight down to Jo'burg. Sophie sat beside Vicki in the bus. 'Do tell,' she said.

Vicki put on her best sphinx-like look, saying she'd reveal all when out of earshot of the others. Well into the flight, after they'd cleared breakfast away, the plane being only half-full, they at last had time to talk. Just the two of them in the rear galley where the engine noise made it hard to overhear intimate conversations, but squeals of laughter could be heard from time to time.

'You didn't.'

'Oh yes I did.'

'What did he do?'

'He did a double take when he saw it was me, but soon cheered up — I'd put on that little red number, the low-cut one. He couldn't take his eyes off me so I was forgiven pretty quickly. We went to that restaurant I told you about. It's very intimate, candles, wine and good food. He had a large steak and I had the fish, Nile perch, they do it in a herby butter and lemon sauce. Really yummy.'

'It's not the food I want to hear about, it's the afters.'

'I'll get to that. We polished off quite a lot of wine, and after coffee and liqueurs we were well oiled. Got back quite late — little before midnight.'

'And?'

'I think you can imagine the rest. He asked if I'd like to go to his room, but I said no as I had an early morning call for the Jo'burg flight. So he said, could he come to my room instead.'

'I led him down the corridor with a little wiggle, then, when we got to my door I kissed him gently on the nose and wished him sweet dreams. I was amazed — he took it like a lamb.'

'Who took it like a lamb?' asked Andy the galley steward, poking his head round the corner. 'You two have been giggling like schoolgirls, I could hear you halfway down the cabin.'

'Oh, just Taff, he took Vicki out last night and tried it on.'

'And did he succeed?'

'No,' said Vicki firmly.

'You were lucky; old Errol doesn't give up easily.'

'You know about Errol?'

'Of course, you must have heard about Delhi. Charlie Payne had us all in fits. The whole fleet knows.'

'We did a swap,' said Sophie, 'he thought he was going out with me.'

'Any skirt in a storm for Errol,' said Andy.

The Honeymoon

Bill Williams found Taff Flynn in the briefing room checking the flight plan, while his captain pored over the weather charts with a new young two ring co-pilot.

'Morning Taff, do we have a final fuel figure yet?'

'Just waiting for the skipper to decide. Have you met Captain White?'

Bill knew him by repute — known as 'Lily White' behind his back. 'Morning, sir. Bill Williams, we haven't flown together before.'

'David White,' he replied, shaking hands and indicating the two-ringer beside him, 'Jim Ford, he's under supervision this trip. I'm sure he'll appreciate all the advice we can give him.'

They discussed the final fuel figure and Bill said he'd go out to the aircraft to start the refuelling.

'I'll go with Bill, if that's OK, skipper,' said Taff, and they left Lily White discussing the basis of his fuel decision with young Jim.

The trip was an interesting mixture of places — Bahrain via Cairo, then a short leg to Karachi, after that, Calcutta and Singapore, with a final stop in Hong Kong. There were a similar number of stops on the way home to London; they would be away for nearly two weeks. The newly introduced 747 fleet had taken over all the prestigious routes to North America, leaving VC10s the interesting places on the old 'Empire routes'. This often meant stopping for several days in the byways of Africa, India and the Far East.

Bill and Taff had completed the pre-flight checks by the time Jim and the skipper came to join them. 'Did you see that new Flight Notice in the book? The one about Moscow?' Taff handed the slim manual to Lily. 'I doubt the KGB will learn much from us.' The notice was entitled 'Crews staying in Moscow'. It advised them, since their hotel rooms were probably bugged, not to refer to the airline's headquarters as 'The Kremlin'. It also warned, in all seriousness, that derogatory remarks might easily be misinterpreted. But crews had always called the large concrete building on the east side of London Airport 'The Kremlin', especially when deriding some damn silly new requirement from the bosses. They were unlikely to change.

'They'll be bugging all our hotel rooms next,' said Bill, 'You'd better watch what you get up to, Taff.' He hoped he'd not guessed who'd been the instigator of the venetian blind incident in Delhi some months before.

'Enough of all that, here's the loadsheet. Let's get down to business.' Lily called for the start checks and they taxied out for take-off. It was dark as they set off; the flight went well, good weather all the way, a quick turn-round in Cairo, and an on-time arrival into Bahrain the following morning. After a day off, they continued to Karachi where they stayed in the BOAC rest house, an old relic from Imperial Airways days. It was a low building with a walkway behind that led out past the pool area to groups of single-storey bedroom blocks. As usual, there were several crews in residence. And, as usual, Taff checked the crew list but there was no one he knew. It being late, he went off to bed disappointed.

Next morning, there was a notice in the lobby advising crews that, due to a cyclone in the Bay of Bengal, there were several changes of plan. All flights to Calcutta and Dacca were cancelled, requiring a number of crew changes. At breakfast, Taff found that Lily had already phoned the airport. Instead of going to Calcutta next day, they would be flying to Singapore via Colombo with a new cabin crew. Taff pretended not to be

BOAC's headquarters and maintenance hangars were designed by Sir Owen Williams and built between 1950 and 1955. The building was officially called Technical Block A, but staff soon dubbed it 'The Kremlin.'

too interested and wondered who they might be. To his delight, who should arrive from Abu Dhabi, but Amanda Berkeley. Neither of them were seen again until next morning.

'Beds OK?' asked Bill innocently during the flight down to Colombo.

Taff complained about the infernal noise from the cockroaches. 'Bloody bugs.'

'KGB bugs more like. Bet the Kremlin have their tabs on you, boyo. Better be careful when you get home. And you won't be much better off in Singapore.'

Taff scowled. In Singapore, the cabin crew stayed downtown in a separate hotel — it would be a single bed again but he hoped no more bugs.

They landed after midnight and agreed to meet for lunch at the Tangle Inn, a mock-Tudor pub a few hundred yards down Orchard Road from their hotel. Taff said he would come too but wouldn't stay for long as he needed a siesta. Bill chaffed him again about single beds, saying it would be better in Hong Kong. 'You go and get your beauty sleep — keep your strength up, like. I'm going to show young Jim lad here the delights of Bugis Street. He's never seen the Kai Tais.'

Lily tut-tutted and warned Bill not to lead Jim astray. 'No place for an innocent abroad.'

It was dark when they took a taxi down to Bugis Street where brightly coloured Chinese signs and paper lanterns hung from the buildings on either side. Delicious smells wafted in the warm tropical air interspersed with a strong smell of drains. Cooks grinned out from behind batteries of sizzling woks. Tourists and sailors still in uniform pushed their way through the crowd. Bill weaved his way expertly to one of his favourite stalls where he sat Jim down at an open-air table and ordered satay, spiced pork ribs, fried noodles, hot Malay curries — washed down with ice-cold Tiger beer.

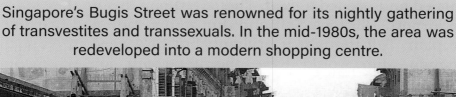

Singapore's Bugis Street was renowned for its nightly gathering of transvestites and transsexuals. In the mid-1980s, the area was redeveloped into a modern shopping centre.

Then the parade of Kai Tais strutting their stuff, with the sailors whistling and leering as they passed. 'Good thing Taff isn't here, they'd be all over 'im.'

'I'd run a mile,' said Jim unable to believe these girls were really men.

Bill sat thoughtfully for a while. 'I've an idea — a solution for all Taff's woes. We all stay together in the Excelsior in Hong Kong and I'm going to get him the best room in the hotel. Old Lily White won't approve so I'm going to need your help.'

'How'll you do that?'

'Tell you tomorrow when I've fixed it.' Now, Bill, like all good flight engineers, could fix almost anything, including hotel rooms for randy pilots. He'd done a few favours in the past for one of the undermanagers at the Excelsior and it was time to call one in.

Next day he phoned the Excelsior and arranged for Taff and Amanda to have the honeymoon suite. He said they were newly married and needed a treat. That afternoon, before they left for the airport, Bill took Taff and Jim to one side and explained the plan. Taff thought it brilliant, but he'd need to persuade Amanda. Jim would have the important job of keeping the captain occupied while the happy couple were whisked upstairs.

Taff and Amanda looked radiant on the flight to Hong Kong, even though they knew they would have to host a crew party in their room. Bill had arranged for an extra supply of champagne, that being an essential part of the deal. That evening, on their arrival at the Excelsior, Taff and Amanda were met by the under-manager who quietly ushered them away, while the rest of the crew checked-in as normal and Jim distracted Lily by asking earnest questions about landing at the notoriously difficult Kai Tak airfield.

At eight o'clock, they all went up to the luxury suite near the top floor to find Taff and Amanda with a white gloved waiter in attendance serving champagne from a trolley loaded with a goodly number of bottles. This was considerably better than the usual crew room party. The view was magnificent, looking out over the typhoon shelter, the Royal Hong Kong Yacht Club, the Noonday Gun, the ships and sampans criss-crossing the harbour and, beyond, the lights of Kowloon. It was fantastic.

More bottles of champers were ordered. Lily, who'd been expecting a normal room party, was horrified but it was too late for him really to object. He spluttered a bit, harrumphed and left, but it was noticed that he'd enjoyed a couple of glasses of champagne. Jokes and tall stories flowed, Taff was called 'Errol', which he seemed to like when it was explained about 'in like Flynn', but Amanda was most unamused. Finally, soon after midnight, people began to drift off to bed. It had been a great party.

The trip back to London went like clockwork. The crew teased the 'honeymooners' unmercifully. Taff kissed Amanda goodbye, and young Jim asked, 'Are all trips out East like that?'

'Only the ones with Errol,' said Bill.

However, the manager of the Excelsior, when he saw how much champagne had been drunk, decided the bill needed to be paid and sent it to the BOAC station manager who, in turn, sent it to the flight manager in London. And so it came to pass, some weeks later, that an official-looking letter arrived at the Flynn residence. Taff opened it at the breakfast table to find that it gently asked if he would be kind enough to settle the account at his earliest convenience.

'What's all that about?' his wife asked.

'Oh, only The Kremlin,' said Taff. 'The boss wants me to call in when I next go to the airport.' But he hadn't seen the enclosed slip of paper fall to the floor.

His wife picked it up. It was a bill from the Excelsior Hotel, made out to Mr and Mrs T A F Flynn in the honeymoon suite, for 1,850 HK$ for champagne.

'Terence,' she exploded. 'And who is *this* Mrs Flynn?' Taff knew this was bad news; she only called him Terence when she was really, really angry.

'Terence, exactly what have you been up to this time?'

'It's that Bill Williams,' said Taff. 'He thought he could play

57

a joke, get us all free champagne. I'll have to get him to sort it out. The letter should really have gone to Bill.'

Two gimlet eyes stared back at him over the breakfast table. 'I don't believe a word. I'm going to phone Bill *and* your flight manager and if I find another girl's been involved, you needn't expect to come back here. You can camp in the rain or go to the pub for all I care.'

Taff had to leave or he'd be late for his next trip.

'Get out now before I throw you out.' She slammed the kitchen door as he picked up his bags. The last words he heard before he closed his front door were his wife on the phone asking to speak to Bill.

He hoped Bill was out. Bad as the bloody KGB, he thought, as he started his car, wondering what to expect when he arrived home next week.

The Village

I was staying upcountry, a Pan-African conference of some sort having filled all the hotels in the city. We had been driven through the night for an hour or so before tumbling gratefully into bed. It had been a long day, we could be anywhere.

When I awoke and drew back the curtains, only a faint light showed in the eastern horizon. Unable to sleep, I dressed and went outside. The stars were slowly fading as I made my way onto the terrace in front of the hotel. It was of a typically 1930s design, but extended more recently in a style that only partly matched the original. A gentle slope led down to the foreshore of a large lake across which, I could just make out some hills on the far side. I wandered slowly down to the water's edge where I found the remains of an old concrete slipway. Around its crumbling end, small multi-coloured fish darted and flashed in the gathering light.

The freshness of the morning air had not yet given way to the heat of a tropical day. There was little point in returning inside, I was on the wrong time zone, sleep had already escaped me, and it was far too early for breakfast. Behind the hotel, a slope of worn grass gave way to the encroaching jungle. The tops of tall trees were just beginning to catch the sunlight. They glowed with the vivid green that is only found in Africa after storms have washed everything clean the night before. Their colour was made even more vivid by the red murram paths below. I followed one of them in among trees that dangled with creepers. I knew not where it would lead but, judging by the many footprints, it was well used.

I must have walked for a mile or two before I came to a clearing. Mealie plants lined the path. Further on, some had been recently cut. A cock crowed, a goat bleated in the distance, and I began to hear the sound of voices. A smell of woodsmoke was intensified by the damp morning air. I rounded a corner and entered a village made of round huts with conical grass roofs. Between the huts, on the beaten earth, chickens scratched, waiting to be fed. A mangy dog of indeterminate parentage came to inspect me. People were emerging from white-painted doorways, stretching in the early morning light. Some children came out, saw me, shot back inside and peeped shyly around the door frame.

Their parents stared at me in astonishment. I politely wished them good morning and was greeted with smiles. Others appeared — the men in tatty khaki shorts, the women in brightly coloured dresses, with some kind of turban or cloth wrapped around their heads. Word must have spread because, soon, others came to look as I made my way between the huts.

A man, considerably older than the rest, came forward. His hair was greying, his face wizened, he lacked a tooth or two but such was his dignity that, had I been wearing a hat, I have no doubt I would have raised it to him. He said some words in a language I did not understand. I wished him good morning in my very British way and apologised for intruding in his village. He seemed to sense the meaning of what I said, or perhaps he was just being polite. He offered his hand; I shook it and wished him well. Everywhere, people smiled and, when I raised my hand in greeting, the men waved back, women nodded shyly, while children stared wide-eyed from behind their hands.

When I came to the edge of village, I turned to look back. There was quite a crowd; the old man gravely raised his right hand. I did the same and entered the forest. I went down the slope along a path which I hoped would lead me back to the lake. Fortunately, it did. When I came to the shore, I followed it back to the hotel. The sun was now well up, soon the heat of the day would be upon me. I mused on what I had seen. Had I been an African, dressed in tribal costume, walking through a remote village in rural England, I wondered whether I would have been greeted with such courteous warmth and grace.

Passengers board a BOAC Boeing 707 at Shannon Airport on the west coast of Ireland.

The Box

Derek Hall loathed the box with a loathing that was visceral. The very thought made his bowels turn to water. His wife, who knew little of aviation, could not understand it. Here was this tall placid man, with whom she had lived for 25 years, reduced to a frightened school boy.

Derek was a genial, competent man. Someone you could rely on to fix the plumbing, repair the mower or drive through rain and storm without turning a hair. He was a keen golfer, with a good handicap, which would have been better had he not been away so much. The years, if anything, had improved his looks — humorous blue eyes flashing from under dark brows, silvery hair contrasting with a good tan, his slim figure declaring a healthy and active life. He was sociable and well liked at the club and in the village.

Penelope, his wife, or Poppy as she preferred to be known, was a large lady, much interested in good works, and strongly independent. She had had to be, with Derek away flying whenever the inevitable domestic crises occurred. She had had to cope with many over the years — rushing young children to hospital after falling out of trees, helping neighbours when the village hall burnt down, sorting out a flood after pipes burst in the roof, rescuing the postman when he had driven into the ditch. She was the sort of person to whom people turned when they needed help.

Everyone saw the Halls as an asset to the village, and it distressed Poppy to see Derek moping around the house and looking distinctly green about the gills. She was glad her friends could not see him like this. Why was it, she asked herself, every six months before he went on the simulator, or whatever it was he did, he started behaving this way? He went off his food. He shut himself away in his study. He bit off her head when she wanted him to do something in the house. Men were such strange creatures, she mused — such fragile egos!

Derek, however, knew his career was on the line every time he went into the box. He loved aeroplanes, he loved flying — and was good at it. He loved the life down the routes with his colleagues. At some of the more exotic stops, he organised adventures with his crew — driving out to interesting places, ancient monuments and natural wonders like waterfalls, mountains, canyons or windswept headlands by the sea. No one who knew him thought him anything other than a confident, adventurous man.

To him, the box was an alien world. He did not like people looking over his shoulder, second-guessing what he should have done and, afterwards, nitpicking his every move. It was like being back at school under the gaze of his tyrannical maths master. It was like being asked to take a driving test again. He knew these sessions in the box were necessary but he hated them. The anxiety made him make mistakes he would never have made down the routes.

In the real world, when events and elements ganged up against him, he relished the challenge. He became ice-cool. Time expanded to give him time to think. He had no difficulty making the right decisions and bringing his fragile craft safely back to earth without ever frightening his passengers. To him, that was important. Passengers should never know they were in an aluminium tube, six miles above the earth, in a hostile environment, travelling at 600 miles an hour. No — they must feel cosseted, safe and pampered in every way. And if anything untoward did happen, they should be delivered back to earth knowing next to nothing of the narrow shave they may have survived. That was his skill, his whole *raison d'être*, and he relished it. Spilled drinks, whether in first class or down the back, were not to be tolerated — ever! Hair-raising escapes were the stuff of bar room chat between fellow pilots.

During his early flying training, he had been a good pupil.

He learnt fast and was confident in the air. But he did suffer a little from 'test-itis'. He knew he could fly well, but tests, with an examiner watching his every move, were a different matter. Unfortunately, a commercial flying career involved countless tests — check flights when training to fly a new aircraft, regular competency checks every six months thereafter, and an annual route check. He never liked them but had always coped. However, recently, he was finding them more and more difficult. He did not know why — was it old age, or was it the dreaded box?

Flight simulators, while being trumpeted by their manufacturers and the airline's training department as being 'exactly like the aircraft', were, for him, more difficult to fly than the real thing. Other pilots felt the same. He found the response to the controls to be slightly different; it made him anxious and it made him struggle. Instead of making smooth adjustments to the controls, he would find himself fighting them. When flying down the radio beam of the instrument landing system (ILS), which guided him through cloud and fog to the runway, he would weave from side to side and wobble up and down, instead of keeping the crossed needles of the ILS neatly centred on the compass in front of him. The harder he tried the worse it became.

His airline arranged these six-monthly simulator sessions on two consecutive days. The first was used for practising various emergency situations. It took the form of a two-hour briefing by an instructor on the technical issues of the day, followed by four hours in the simulator during which the two pilots flew, in turn, the various manoeuvres they had discussed. They were demanding but satisfying training exercises. The following day had a similar format, but with the instructor acting as an examiner checking that they flew to the exacting standards required. It was these sessions that Derek had come to loathe.

When the day arrived, the first session went well. The young co-pilot he was teamed up with was competent and helpful. The instructor was affable and keen that they should both do well; his whole manner was one of calm encouragement.

Derek felt relaxed and confident, coping well with each of the flying manoeuvres and emergencies that had been thrown at him. He felt happy until he saw the roster for the next day. The training captain who would be taking his check was someone he thoroughly disliked. The man was known to be a martinet, with a superior manner and loud booming voice. It was enough to intimidate even the hardiest of souls.

That night, he went to bed thoroughly out of sorts. He slept badly, woke in the early hours, made some tea, sat in his study and mentally rehearsed the things he would have to do during the check. At breakfast, he ate little. His wife knew better than to try to cheer him up — when in one of these moods he was best left alone. He arrived at the training centre feeling tired and nervous.

The check got off to a bad start when the training captain asked a number of technical questions which Derek fluffed. He knew that he knew the answers but they came out all wrong. In the simulator he had difficulty levelling out at the correct altitude after take-off. But he calmed himself down, managed the short airways flight OK, and was pleased with his first ILS approach and landing.

The next part was not so good. He handled the engine failure on take-off very nicely, keeping the aircraft climbing straight ahead and at the correct speed, but when he came round for the approach and landing, his problems began. On three engines, the Boeing 707 was not so easy to fly; every time he adjusted power he had to balance the asymmetric thrust with a judicious amount of rudder control. Could he keep the ILS needles centralised? No. He began to weave from side to side, the more he concentrated the worse it became. Then, as he descended on the glide slope towards the runway, he found himself either too high or too low. Sweat dripped off his nose, his eyes blurred, he chased the needles but, however hard he tried, he could not centralise them. He began to despair.

At last, when he broke out below the cloud, he saw the runway far off to one side, but he was too low to make an 'S-turn' towards it. He opened up the power and climbed away.

A BOAC Boeing 707-436.

The training captain said nothing. What next? He dreaded the answer. Visions of failure stabbed his brain — the humiliation, how could he face his colleagues again, how could he face his wife? More sweat ran down his face. His shirt was soaking, his palms were slippery, and his right leg ached as he held full rudder against the power of the good engines on that side.

The training captain suggested, in lofty tones, that perhaps he should have another go and, this time, do it better. He manoeuvred the aircraft for another approach. Once again, he started the descent down the ILS towards the runway. Once again, the needles blurred. Once again, he struggled to keep them centred. And once again, thoughts of failure destroyed his concentration. But — but — this time, he just managed to find the runway and land. When the aircraft came to a stop, he sat there limp and drained. He knew he had failed.

He had never failed a check flight before. He was exhausted. He was utterly depressed. How would this affect his career, would he lose his confidence, would he still have a job, how would he cope? The training captain suggested they leave the simulator and go to the briefing room; there were things they needed to discuss.

The young co-pilot was sent on his way with a good report. Derek stayed behind to meet his fate. The training captain slowly, and in great detail, went through all his mistakes, but ended his written report with the words, 'he eventually reached the required standard'. He then looked at Derek a little more sympathetically and asked what the problem was. Was it medical, was it eyesight, were there difficulties at home? Obviously, there was something wrong. Derek could think of no excuse and waited. The final verdict was that he should be interviewed by the flight training manager before he flew again.

Derek went home with his tail between his legs. His wife took one look at him and poured him a stiff Scotch. She could not understand what had happened; this was a good deal worse than usual. He explained he was to be interviewed by the training manager and phoned to arrange an appointment for the next day. Best get it over with as soon as possible.

Sleep would not come that night. He wondered what he would do if he was sacked. His whole life had been flying; he had never thought about anything else. He woke from a bad dream in which he had chased those bloody needles all over the sky, so he must have slept a little.

When he arrived outside the training manager's office, he was offered a coffee but, instead, asked only for a glass of water — his mouth was so dry. The training manager came out, invited him in and ushered him into a chair. Instead of being interviewed across the desk he found himself being asked a series of sympathetic questions. He had always had a good flying record, everyone knew he was a good pilot, there was no question whatsoever of a bollocking; the important thing was to find out what was wrong, fix it and have him flying again. An appointment with the company doctors had already been arranged for later that morning, it was probably something quite simple.

A thorough medical examination revealed only that he needed to start wearing glasses. He should have done it sooner had he not been so vain. And, the doctor suggested, perhaps a week off duty would help restore his wellbeing.

His wife said only that she had known for several years he needed glasses. She could not think why he had been so silly. She hoped also, in future, he would not make such a fuss about the box.

The White Mustang

I'm a country girl, never really wanted to be in London, but my father insisted. 'Go stay with your aunts, get a proper job.' He trained racehorses near Lambourn. 'There's more to life than riding. And the way you ride, you'll end up breaking your neck. Anyway, you might meet some nice young men.' But London in winter was cold and grey. I longed for fresh air, wide open spaces and fast gallops on spirited horses.

The aunts were OK but I wanted more freedom. 'Will you be in tonight, dear?' And 'Who was that young man we saw you with yesterday?' They were kind and meant well — but, rents off Sloane Street, where I worked, were so expensive, I needed to look elsewhere. Every evening, I scoured the *Evening Standard* and was beginning to lose hope, when I saw a small ad' from two girls wanting a third to join them. They lived in Barons Court, five stops from Knightsbridge, my nearest tube station, so I decided to investigate.

It was a dank Saturday afternoon in February, nearly dark, when I walked down the street and knocked on the door of the redbrick Victorian terraced house where they lived. The door was opened by a girl in a loose pink kaftan, her hair tied in a towel like a turban. 'Oh,' she said, leading me up the stairs, 'we were expecting you later.'

'I'm so sorry, you were easier to find than I thought. And it's so cold outside I hoped you wouldn't mind if I was early.'

'I'm Pat, this is Jackie.' She took me into their small sitting room. 'You'd better take the chair, the sofa has a spring coming through.'

I looked around at the meagre furniture: sofa in front of the gas fire, armchair to one side, a record player in the opposite corner surrounded by scattered records, books and magazines, and a small dining table against the far wall.

'Jackie'll show you round, I've just got to finish my hair. Then we can discuss rents and things.'

I followed Jackie down the corridor, she was tall and dark, with an elegant swan neck, rather like Ava Gardner. She looked gorgeous in a tight sweater and slacks.

'This is Pat's room, mine is the one over here,' she said, pointing out the two bedrooms, the first containing a bed and small chest of drawers, the other, two single beds and a dressing table. 'I hope you don't mind sharing with me, it's a bit cramped but further away from the noise.' And as if to emphasise the point, a train rattled past the window as she showed me the kitchen, tiny bathroom and loo.

'That's all there is I'm afraid. Why don't we go back to the sitting room and wait for Pat. She'll be out in a minute.'

I sat down in the only chair while Jackie curled up on the sofa, tucking her long legs back under a cushion. 'What do you do?' I asked.

'I'm a Bunny Girl,' she said. 'Work most evenings, usually back around four in the morning. And you?'

My eyes nearly popped out of my head. 'Just a secretary, in a solicitor's office, nine to five. And Pat?'

'She's a stewardess with BOAC, hardly ever here. She's off early tomorrow morning, that's why she's doing her hair. Won't be back for a week. Somewhere out east.'

At which point, Pat returned, totally transformed, looking cool and elegant, her blonde hair held in a neat French roll.

'I've brought us some tea,' she said, and began to pour like a proper hostess while we continued discussing rent and living arrangements. 'Well, looks like it could work rather well. I'm away all the time. Jackie sleeps during the day. She'll be out when you're sleeping — almost like hot bunking! What d'you think?'

We agreed to give it a try for three months and I'd move in the following week.

As I went home to the aunts, I wondered how I would fit in. The girls both looked so glamorous. Me, I'm just Rosemary, up from the country, plain brown hair, go to work in a white blouse, pearls — fake, unfortunately, but you'd never know — a grey pencil slim skirt and black high heels. But despite my fears, we soon slipped into an easy routine.

In fact, it worked rather well. Each morning, I dressed quietly in the sitting room so as not to wake Jackie, and each evening she went out to the Bunny Club when I came in. We never got in each other's way and I rarely heard her coming back in the early hours. Pat, on the other hand, came and went to no fixed schedule. When she was away, we had the place to ourselves. When she was home she was either sleeping off her jetlag, or out somewhere.

Then, one sunny Saturday morning in June, Jackie said, 'C'mon Rosie, time you stopped talking about it. Be brave, take the plunge.'

For several weeks, I'd been going on about the miniskirts I'd seen in the King's Road. At work, I was obliged to wear sober

The King's Road in the 1960s.

Imogen Waterhouse and Lizzy Jagger modelling 1970s BOAC cabin crew uniforms to mark the 80th Anniversary of British Airways flights to Hong Kong.

clothes, the partners having very decided ideas of how their secretaries and receptionist should look — demure and elegant as befitting a respectable firm of solicitors. But I wanted to break out. After all, this was the Swinging Sixties.

The King's Road was where it all happened. We went from shop to shop looking at snazzy little numbers, Jackie egging me on, finding shorter and shorter skirts and dresses, though I baulked at the hot pants.

'Well, what about this?' Jackie pulled out a fuchsia pink mini dress. 'Try that, it'd be fab with a white belt and boots. I know just the place round the corner for the boots.'

I bought the lot. And then blew the money my father had given me on an absolutely gorgeous blue and purple tunic dress from Biba. Wow, did I feel good. 'Let's celebrate. How about the coffee bar over there?'

'I think,' said Jackie, dabbing some frothy cream from her upper lip, 'you should definitely wear the pink one to work. Those old jossers in your office need some pizzazz.' But I could see old Mr Bentham having apoplexy.

'No. They'd huff and puff, I'd be lectured about declining morals and they'd probably send me straight home.'

'More likely they'd be turned on like some of the blokes in the Bunny Club.'

'Tell me more?' I asked, 'About the men at the club? Do you have to fend them off in droves?'

'Gawd, where *do* I start? Not so much in the club, we've very strict rules. No dating, no drinking on the job. But you do get pats on the bum, lecherous stares down your cleavage. Even try to pull your pompoms off and drop things on the floor to see if you'll bend down.'
'Bet that's awkward!'

'Not really.' Jackie showed me the famous 'Bunny Dip'. 'It's so your boobs don't pop out. 'Course, you're expected to show off your assets, but not that much. It's all rather pathetic really, 'specially when they try to pick you up outside after. That's why I always come home by taxi.'

'I was asked out to lunch by one of our clients the other day. He was rather nice, seemed very well heeled'.

'You'd better watch out,' she said. 'If he's anything like my lot, he'll only be after one thing.'

'He's not like that at all,' I protested. 'I'm going out with him again this evening. He's Scottish, he's called Donald and he likes horses.'

I'm not sure Jackie approved.

That evening I wore my new pink outfit. Donald had only seen me in my sober work clothes before and he *did* approve. He invited me to a party the next weekend being given by his uncle. It would be rather smart, why didn't I come in the mini dress? I said I'd wear my new Biba number if he'd come in a kilt. He wasn't so sure about that. But when he picked me

In 1967, BOAC introduced the paper dress for flights between New York and the Caribbean. Manufactured by Joseph Lore, bonded paper clothing was a new idea for cheap, disposable wear. The dress was meant to be worn once, and then discarded.

In 1970, BOAC introduced new stewardess uniforms designed by Clive of London (Clive Evans). The style reflected the space-age fashion of the 1960s with rigid geometric lines.

up outside our flat in his sports car, I was glad to see he was wearing it. I was rather sorry the other girls weren't there; they would have been most impressed.

The party was in a house in Queen's Gardens, Bayswater — a quiet leafy road to the north of Hyde Park. I thought it rather hilarious, the two of us disentangling ourselves from a low-slung sports car in our 'dresses' and climbing up the steps to such a posh front door. I didn't say so and tried not to giggle. At that time, I didn't know him well enough.

'Uncle Alastair's a QC in Hong Kong,' Donald explained. 'This is his London home. He's here for a few weeks catching up with old friends in the City. You'll like him, he's a bachelor, bit eccentric, but likes young people and is good fun despite his age.'

A butler answered the door and showed us upstairs. Uncle Alastair greeted us warmly, eyeing me up and down appreciatively. He was shorter than Donald, rather plump, with a round face under similar sandy hair, a friendly smile but with a sharp eagle eye.

'Your usual?' he said handing Donald a whisky. 'And for you, my dear?'

'A dry sherry, please.'

They excused themselves for a moment to discuss some family matters before the other guests arrived. I admired the room, its high ceiling and the windows looking out onto the trees across the road. On the wall to the right, above a marble fireplace, hung a large painting of a castellated grey stone house in a wooded glen; I wondered if it was the family home. Below, on the mantelpiece, was a carriage clock, some Chinese porcelain and family photos in silver frames. In front of the fireplace, set round an oriental rug, were two faded sofas and some comfy armchairs. An antique table behind the sofa held more photos — men in exotic places — China, India, the Middle East, Cairo perhaps? The opposite wall was lined with bookshelves. And in an alcove, at the back, opposite the windows, stood a fat bronze Buddha.

The clock struck seven. Laughter rose up the stairs, people

started gathering and I went over to the window to watch the new arrivals. They were all well dressed.

A car drew up. I'm not up on cars, but it looked like a Bentley. The chauffeur opened the rear door and a girl stepped out, followed by a man of distinctly Eastern appearance. I recognised her instantly, it was the cool Grace Kelly look that gave her away. It was Pat! I drew back from the window and, at that moment, Donald took my elbow, steering me towards some of his friends, mainly legal people who clearly knew each other well, but they welcomed me in.

They must have thought me rather shy or perhaps stand-offish, because I fear I was more interested in Pat. She looked her usual cool self, attracting admiring glances as she and her man joined a group of oldies on the far side of the room.

'Who are they?' I asked.

'Oh, some of Uncle Alastair's city friends.'

'And the man with the blonde girl?'

'Lebanese banker I think — and one of his many girls.' And they continued talking about some people they knew.

'Donald tells me you're interested in horses,' said one young man. I told him about Lambourn and my father training race horses. 'Over the sticks or the flat?' He knew of him and we talked horses for a while. Like me, he lived and breathed horses, rode in point-to-points and followed National Hunt racing. 'I'm surprised you're in London, you must miss all that.'

I agreed but said it would only be for a few years; I didn't say my father hoped I would meet some suitable young men. I looked across at Pat again, she was wearing some very flashy earrings. She caught my eye and looked quickly away. Then I was caught up in the horsey discussion again. Several others in the group also followed racing — mainly flat racing, which I thought boring but didn't say so.

Donald, being the perfect gentleman, introduced me to some more friends. We talked pleasantly enough but with little in common. Soon, I found myself standing behind Pat. Her man had his hand on her back in a familiar way. Suddenly she turned and, seeing me, hissed, 'You don't know me.' I nodded but not before seeing that her necklace was even more magnificent than her earrings. Fortunately, Uncle Alastair rescued me, oblivious to the interchange.

'What's all this about horses?' he boomed. 'Can't stand 'em myself. Dangerous beasts, always biting and kicking.'

'Not if you know how to handle them.'

'And they keep getting colic or something.'

'That's only if you don't feed them properly,' I protested.

'Did I hear food?' said Donald. 'It's time we left, we have a dinner date.' And he looked meaningfully at his uncle.

'Well, you'd better feed *her* properly — and see she doesn't get colic.' He looked at me warmly and mumbled something to Donald about a good gallop.

'What was that he said?' I asked when we were back in the car.

'Oh — he recommended oysters.'

'I wonder why,' I replied going a little pink.

Clearly, Uncle Alastair appreciated pretty girls. After dinner, which did not include oysters, Donald drove me home, squeezed my hand, gave me a warm kiss on the cheek and asked to see me again.

But I noticed Pat did not come home that night, nor the next two and, when she did, she went straight to bed, woke early next morning and left for another of her trips to exotic places.

It was several days before I had an opportunity to talk to Jackie.

'Good party? What's he like, do tell?'

'Rather sweet.'

'Didn't try it on, then?'

'No. Much too much of a gentleman. We had a quiet dinner after and then he brought me home.'

'Those are the ones you have to watch,' was all she said.

Then I told her about Pat. It seemed Jackie had had her suspicions for a while. Never here, often tired and always mysterious was her opinion. Can only be one thing: men.

I said she didn't look the type. But Jackie said I was just an innocent country girl and wouldn't know about things like that.

Then one evening, about a week later, an open-top white Ford Mustang drew up outside our flat in Barons Court Road and Pat stepped out.

'Whose is the car?' we asked as she came in.

'Mine,' she said, and vanished to her room.

'Well!' we both exclaimed in unison — and I added, 'I wonder how she earned that?'

'Shssss. I'll give you two guesses,' said Jackie.

I giggled. A train rumbled along the line at the back of the house, a car honked somewhere out in the front.

We heard her rummaging about. She came out with her suitcase and said, 'I thought you'd both be out. Oh, well, I may's well tell you. Marc gave it to me, and we're going away for the weekend.' With that she disappeared downstairs and roared off towards the traffic lights at the end of the road.

Over the next few months, Pat came and went as usual, though we saw much less of her. Out in the road, the car caused quite a flutter, attracting envious looks from young men and small boys. White Mustangs were rather rare in Barons Court.

'D'you know what happened last Wednesday night?' said Jackie from behind her magazine.

'No.'

It was a Sunday morning, Pat was away on a trip again, and Jackie and I were lazing around in our dressing gowns drinking coffee, reading, gossiping, listening to records.

'Pat was at the Playboy Club — haven't seen her there before — with a man at the bar, but she didn't see me, 'cos I was round a corner. Oldish bloke he was, they looked very cosy together. But — it didn't go down at all well with one of the punters in the casino. Middle Eastern type, rather smooth.'

'Was he dark and slim? The punter I mean.'

'Yes, sort of. Wore dark glasses indoors.'

'Oh, oh,' I said, 'that's Marc, he was with her at that party I went to with Donald.'

'That explains it. Because he suddenly stopped playing, went very quiet, threw all his cards down on the table and stalked over to them. Pat didn't see him coming. Picked up her G & T, poured it down her cleavage and left. Pat went white.

There was quite a commotion, that's all I saw. Bloody funny, I thought!'

Next morning, early, Pat returned from her trip, parked outside as usual and sloped off to bed. I left for work, but when I came home all hell had broken out. There was quite a gathering round the car. Pat was leaning against the bonnet and Marc was in the road shouting at her. As I slipped past, trying not to be noticed, all I heard was Pat saying, 'You can't have them.'

Upstairs in the flat, I joined Jackie by the window to watch the fracas below. Pat was waving the car keys above her head taunting Marc. But, with a look of triumph, he merely walked round her, put his hand in his pocket, took out a second set, climbed into the car, revved the engine several times and screeched off.

'Serves her right,' said Jackie. 'My father always said you couldn't tame a Mustang.'

A 1965 Ford Mustang in Wimbledon White.

As a reminder of the Golden Age of travel, in 2019, British Airways repainted a Boeing 747-400 in BOAC's iconic blue and gold livery.

The Road to Kandy

We sat on the terrace of the hotel looking out over the sea. The sun, setting fast behind golden thunderheads, cast long shadow beams high up across the sky. Coconut palms swished above our heads, while the sea sucked and gurgled on the rocks below. To our right, the beach stretched northwards towards Colombo and the docks. Groups of fishermen were drawing in nets that curved out into the waves, we speculated on what their catch might be. Everywhere, people thronged the beach enjoying the sea breeze after the heat of the day, the women in colourful saris.

James had lived much of his life out East, his father before him, and also his grandfather. Now, long retired, Ceylon was his permanent home. He had been born on that beautiful island before the war, where his father had managed tea estates near Nuwara Eliya. Like most children of British parents, he was sent home to boarding school when he was eight. He had not seen his parents again until after the war, in 1946, and then only occasionally, when they took their leave in England. After independence, they had stayed on. He had remained in England.

It had been a lonely upbringing, but it stood him in good stead when he joined BOAC. He had progressed up the commercial side, enjoying many postings around the world, mainly in the Levant, the Far East and Africa. He was a good mixer, but content with his own company. I first met him in Bahrain when he was a station officer and I a new co-pilot on VC10s. We liked each other immediately; there was something about his slim graceful build, his finely drawn face, dark brown eyes, flashing smile and animated talk which was unusually beguiling. Now, sitting beside me, smiling gently, with his silver hair and much wrinkled face, he looked the very picture of a cultured Englishman in the tropics.

Our paths had crossed many times. I used to take him things he was unable to buy abroad. In return, he would invite me home to dine in his various temporary homes, furnished always in sparse company style. At one time I think he must have been lonely, though he never admitted it. He married fairly late in life, a Scotswoman from Kenya. She was as welcoming as her husband, adding many homely touches to his previous Spartan existence. They had had no children and she had died some years before he retired to Ceylon. There, he had met and married Anna, a Singhalese, with whom he now lived happily in the hills above Kandy.

He was clearly glad to see me after so many years and we talked about times past. He was brimming with amusing stories of life in small communities: embassy parties, business gatherings, petty rivalries in clubs, the foibles of people living in faraway places, always aware that he was 'Mr. BOAC', representing the lifeline home. He touched on little incidents, like when a pompous businessman raised Cain at check-in, demanding special treatment while shouting, 'Do you know who I am?' and the exasperated girl behind the desk picking up the Tannoy to announce, 'Can anyone help me, I have a gentleman here who doesn't know who he is?' There was hell to pay for that. And then the Sheik, with his entourage of wives, demanding the whole first class section and the Brits outraged at the indignity of being downgraded.

We dined in the main restaurant, a high-ceilinged white-painted room, lined with classical pillars and graceful arched windows. It was cool inside, the service excellent, the local fish delicious. James talked about the civil war which, thankfully, was now over. He was distressed that so beautiful an island could harbour such savagery; how could such things happen in a country where most of the people were Buddhist?

After dinner, we returned to the terrace with our whisky and sodas and continued to reminisce. His life had been more

At the heart of Kandy is the scenic Kandy (Bogambara) Lake.

varied than mine. Whereas he had lived for several years in each country to which he had been posted, I had merely flown through, skimming the surface of cultures in which he had been immersed. Suddenly he asked me, 'Do you believe in fate?'

'No, I don't. Chance, definitely. The lottery of life, yes — and in taking sound precautions.'

'There speaks the wise aviator.'

'Why do you ask?'

'Perhaps because I've been blessed with so much luck.'

'For that matter, so have I. Thirty-five years flying and never scratched an aeroplane.'

'No.' He paused. 'I was thinking of something much deeper than that. You see,' and he paused again, 'I've always left places before bad things happened.

'My family were in Malaya shortly before the Japanese arrived. My father had been sent there to help in the new tea plantations. Let me think — that would have been in '36. Mother took me to England three years later and left me there while she went back to Malaya to be with my father. Fortunately, they returned to Ceylon when his secondment ended in '41. Didn't see 'em again 'til after the war.'

'That must've been hard.'

'Yes, very. They called us 'Raj Orphans'. I was fortunate to stay with some maiden aunts during the holidays. By the end of my schooling I knew them better than my parents. You needed to develop a hard carapace to survive, but it was good training for life in BOAC. D'y'know, when I first went to England, Singhalese was almost my mother tongue? I'm good at languages, always picked 'em up easily. So, after school, it seemed an obvious choice to read Modern Languages. Did three years at King's College, London, including a few months in Germany before graduating. I was able to defer National Service until after university — they sent me to Berlin as an interpreter. That was a bit of an eye-opener so soon after the war. Thank heavens I went there rather than Korea. Didn't want to be a soldier — a civil career seemed a better way to see the world, so I joined BOAC. One of the best things I ever did. My first posting was Cairo, which I left in '56, just before the Suez Crisis. They bombed the airport y'know.'

I ordered more whisky and soda and asked where he went next.

'Beirut. Wonderful place in its heyday. Then I knocked around a few other places in the Middle East — Damascus, Baghdad — and Bahrain, where I met you. Then out to Tokyo — the Far East, where I'd always wanted to be. I loved it, especially the Japanese gardens and temples. But I was only there a year when I had the first big escape of my life. D'you remember our 707, the one that broke up over Fuji? I was supposed to be on it.' He lapsed into silence.

'How come?'

'March '66, a Canadian Pacific DC8 crashed at Haneda. It was late evening; the pilot had already made one approach but couldn't land because of the poor visibility. On his second approach, he hit the approach lights and sea wall. Only eight passengers survived. I was on duty at the time and was roped in to help. Saved my life. I was due to fly out to Hong Kong next day. But having been up all night, I overslept and missed the flight. Two crashes in two days, it was horrible.'

'1966,' I said. 'What a year. I had a narrow escape too, only a month after you.'

'In an aircraft?'

'Yup, but that's another story.'

'Did I ever tell you about something that happened back in '51? I was still at King's. My parents had wangled an air ticket to Ceylon. I flew out on a BOAC Argonaut and was taking the bus up to Kandy to meet them. D'y know the road?'

I shook my head.

'When you leave Colombo, it's flat for about thirty miles or so, you pass small villages, roadside shanties, bullock carts, ancient lorries; everywhere there are coconut palms, trees of all sorts, the land's rich, everything grows like mad. It's idyllic, it's lush. You see elephants being scrubbed in rivers, water buffalo in fields, chickens running across the road. It's a wonderful country, I love it. So vibrant after the drabness of London. Then the road starts to climb, winding up through the hills. Kandy's around fifteen hundred feet up, it's cool and lush. Nuwara Eliya, where my parents lived, is even higher, nearly six thousand feet. Much like Scotland — Scots pines, mock Tudor houses, misty mountains with manicured tea estates instead of heather.

'We were climbing slowly through the hills when the bus jerked to a stop halfway round a bend. It was a dilapidated old thing. I thought the engine had failed. But no — it was a snake. I was sitting at the front behind the driver and saw it clearly. The largest I've ever seen, it stretched right across the road. The driver waited a good ten minutes while this shiny brown monster slid across into the bushes. Only when it had completely disappeared, did he start the engine and grind on up the hill towards Kandy. While we were waiting, I asked him why he'd stopped. Most Brits I knew would have run over it.

'He was small man, old, bent, at least he seemed old to me — bear in mind I was only nineteen. He had a wise, slow smile. He took a while to answer my question and then said it was because he was a Buddhist and revered life. "Don't kill unless you to have to. Only two reasons to kill — to eat or save your life. Respect nature. We are all one — animals, birds, insects, even snakes. All life is one. If you kill something, you kill part of yourself".'

'What, all that from an ordinary bus driver?'

'He may have been only a bus driver but he was anything but ordinary. He seemed to embody all the wisdom of the East,' James answered. 'In those few words, he described a whole philosophy. And then he added something I've always remembered. 'If you want a charmed life, you must not kill.' And d'you know? I've never killed anything with equanimity — ever since.'

'Are you implying that's why you missed the flight in Tokyo? Come on, you either have good luck or bad luck — curtains.'

'It's not as simple as that. I've had too many narrow escapes. It's more than luck. I've always left places before a calamity.'

89

BOAC had a reputation for excellent cabin service.

'Aren't you exaggerating a bit? We all have lucky escapes. I could tell you some of mine. Are you trying to tell me there's more to it than that?'

'Yes, I'm sure of it. Living here I'm surrounded by Buddhist history. It's ancient, it's everywhere. Dagobas at Anuradhapura. Buddha's left footprint on Adam's Peak. The Temple of the Tooth in Kandy. Ever been there?' I had to admit I hadn't. 'It contains a relic — Tooth of the Buddha — revered throughout Ceylon. Anna and I were looking for a house up in the hills. We'd found a small apartment behind the Queen's Hotel while we were house-hunting. It was convenient, near the shops, but rather noisy, but I liked it because it was near the lake where I could walk along the shore. Always been an early riser. Dawn's the best time of the day in the tropics.

'Well — on that morning, I woke at five. Impossible to get back to sleep, so it seemed a good time for a walk; went out much earlier than usual, it was still dark. I walked towards the Temple, past the road block where the police knew me well by then, they let me through. For some reason, I didn't go far, don't know why, and turned back when I reached the Queen's Bath. I was halfway home when an enormous explosion knocked me flat. There was broken glass everywhere, and clouds of smoke and dust rising above the Temple. I couldn't think what had happened.'

Did I remember it? Yes, it had hit the news, people had been killed and injured, much of the entrance area had been destroyed but the holy relic of the tooth was safe. Knowing that James was living in Kandy, I remembered hoping he had been OK but never guessed he had been that close. I also remembered the anger that such desecration had caused. I tried to remember the date.

'January '98, a few days before the 50th Independence celebrations. Another lucky escape. If I hadn't gone out so early and if I hadn't turned back when I did, I would've been killed. It made me think back to that bus driver. Was there something in what he'd said? I've always tried to lead a good life. Even did what he said; never killed anything unless I had to. Perhaps the way one leads one's life really does influence its course. I began to think so. I've always lived modestly, never done things to excess, tried to do good unto others. Was that why I'd been spared? So I started reading Buddhist texts. I sought out monks and talked to them. It certainly made me think.'

James looked at me, searching my face for some sign of agreement. I knew him to be a good man. I didn't want to hurt his feelings. Me? I'm not religious. I'd describe myself as agnostic — I simply don't know. Belief and atheism imply certitude. I only feel certain about things I can see, touch and prove. I admire the scientific method — observation, theory, testing, proof — and even then, nothing is absolutely certain. There's always another theory.

'Just like you, I believe in leading a good life,' I said. 'But I don't see how that can affect the future. To a certain extent, you create your own luck. Eternal vigilance, always being aware of your surroundings, looking for the minute signs that spell danger. In flying, we call it situational awareness.'

'I still think there's much more to it than that,' James mused. 'Six years ago, Anna and I went down to the coast for Christmas; we'd booked into a small beach hotel in Hambantota with the idea of staying until the New Year. It was beautiful by the sea. Cool at that time of year — well, relatively so. The Christmas lunch was sumptuous, we had a feast and needed a siesta. While we were resting, Anna began to complain of a gippy tummy, she wanted to go home. Reluctantly, we decided to cut short our stay and leave early next morning. I thought it wise to have the best part of the day for the drive up through the mountains to Kandy. So, we were up at dawn and left before eight. We went north past the airport towards Wellawaya and got home late that afternoon. Anna went to lie down. I wandered into the sitting room and put on the TV — couldn't believe what I saw. The whole south coast devastated by the tsunami. I learnt later our hotel had been flattened shortly after we'd left. I know you are a sceptic — but three narrow escapes — that's not luck.'

'Well, I know an old bomber pilot who survived three tours without a scratch,' I said. 'And he was no angel. What were the odds on that?'

'Perhaps he was blessed in ways we don't know. In Buddhism there is the concept of leading the 'right life'; they call it The Eightfold Path — right action, right intentions, right mindfulness, right speech — things like that. They also have a profound reverence for life. All life is one — as the bus driver said. But more interesting for me is the Law of Karma — what you do now affects your whole future life. That's what I have been contemplating recently. I think I may have been blessed because I have tried to lead a right life. And it's more than just those three escapes. There were lots of other things, little things, nothing like as significant. I was in Lagos when the Biafran War started but was posted to Entebbe before they shot up the office. Uganda was beautiful, but I was posted away before Idi Amin ruined the place. I was in Teheran just before the revolution. And then Kuwait — I left the day before Saddam invaded.'

I saw his point. 'Just as long as you don't believe in reincarnation,' I said. I liked him too much to argue.

'Come; it's late,' he said. 'Tomorrow we'll drive up the road to Kandy past the elephants bathing in the river. You'll see the brilliant red 'Flame of the Forest' trees, breathe the smell of the jungle and the heady perfume of the frangipani; they call it the Temple Tree. And I'll show you where I saw the snake. We can visit the Temple of the Tooth and, perhaps, talk to some monks. Anna is longing to meet you, you'll like her.'

Mayday, Mayday, Mayday!

June 1987. Vancouver International Airport. Weather good — a warm summer evening, light westerly winds, good visibility, and a cloud base at 2000 feet. A Boeing 747 is turning onto the runway ready for take-off. Everything is normal — the flight crew, George Grey, Brian Martin and John Parslow, are running through the last of their litany of drills and checks.

'Before take-off check complete, Skip,' says John, the flight engineer, from his seat behind the two pilots.

'Speedbird 200, clear take-off, wind 250 at 15 knots.' This, the routine instruction from Air Traffic Control (ATC). Ahead lay a flight of 4,150 nautical miles to London, Heathrow.

Captain George Grey takes a quick look round the cockpit to ensure all is as it should be. 'OK — everyone ready? Standing them up.' He pushes the four thrust levers forward until they are vertical, then pauses, to allow the engines to spool up.

'Speedbird 200 rolling,' Brian, his co-pilot, confirms to ATC, as they slowly begin their take-off roll down runway 26L.

'Engines stable,' calls John.

'Set power,' responds George, pushing the thrust levers further forward to apply full power while John makes minor adjustments to ensure exactly the right power is set on each of the four engines.

Brian concentrates on the airspeed indicator. 'Airspeed building.' A pause — then, '80 knots.' They continue to accelerate, the runway streaming past the cockpit windows faster and faster. 'Vee one,' he calls again. This is the decision speed after which it is impossible to stop on the runway if anything goes wrong. George removes his right hand from the thrust levers.

Vancouver International Airport.

'Rotate.'

George eases back on the control column and they lift off on their way to London. Suddenly the aircraft shudders. A series of loud bangs comes from one of the engines. The fire warning bell sounds. The heavy 747 lurches to the left forcing George to push hard on the right rudder pedal to keep the aircraft straight.

'Vee two,' calls Brian and presses the master warning light to silence the bell. George focuses all his attention on maintaining V2, the correct climb-out speed — neither too fast nor too slow. Optimum speed is critical now. It has to be exactly right for the best climb gradient.

'Positive climb.'

'Gear up,' orders George. Brian reaches forward and moves the gear lever on the instrument panel to the up position to retract the undercarriage.

Suddenly another bang shakes the aircraft, then another and another, followed by a horrible rattling noise.

'Fire warning on number one engine,' shouts John. 'And we're losing power on number two.'

'Shit!' mutters George. Then aloud, 'Wait till we get to 400 feet.' After what seems an age, he says, 'OK, 400 feet. Now. What's the situation on those engines?'

'Number one's still on fire,' John replies, 'and we've lost all power on number two.'

'OK — fire drill number one engine.' Then, to leave Brian and John free to deal with the engine fire, George adds, 'My R/T,' and calls ATC on the radio-telephone, 'Mayday, Mayday, Mayday, Speedbird 200, two of my engines have failed. We're climbing straight ahead. Standby.'

The co-pilot and flight engineer go through the well-rehearsed fire drill, closing the thrust lever, switching off the fuel supply, pulling the fire handle on the panel above their heads and pressing the button to fire the extinguisher within the cowling into the engine. John reads out the checklist to confirm each item has been completed. 'Fire drill complete on number one engine, the fire's out. Shall I shut down the number two?'

'Is it giving any power?' George asks.

'No.'

'OK, shut it down.' George very gently nurses the stricken aircraft upwards on its reluctant climb. Though the shaking and shuddering is diminishing, they are still only a few hundred feet above the water.

Moreover, not far ahead, as George well knows, lie the mountains of Vancouver Island. On a clear day they are magnificent but not today with so much cloud around. 'Tell ATC I may have to turn slightly towards the north to stay over the water clear of high ground.'

Brian does so. Then ATC calls, 'Speedbird 200, Vancouver Tower. We saw you hit some birds on take-off, also fire on your left side from one of the engines. What are your intentions?'

To stay airborne is the unspoken thought! 'We're only just managing to climb. We need to start dumping fuel.'

'OK, Speedbird. Change to Departure Control. We've advised them about your mayday.'

Slowly the aircraft edges upwards. George's right leg is locked rigid on the rudder pedals as he strains to keep the aircraft straight. After what seems another age, they reach 1,000 feet. George lowers the nose a degree or two to start accelerating. Gradually, as the speed increases, they retract the wing flaps, stage by stage and, once they are in, begin again to climb.

'Right,' George says, 'let's review. She's flying OK. I've wound in full rudder trim and reduced the power slightly. She's climbing better now, and easier to keep straight. We're visual, we've got clear water ahead. No obstacles. It's safe on this heading for a while. In a moment, Brian, I'll hand over to you. Tell me when you're ready.'

Brian settles himself more comfortably in his seat. 'OK, I'm ready. I have control.'

'You have control. Keep her climbing straight ahead. Stay parallel with the shore line. Don't try any turns yet. I'll stay on the R/T and tell ATC what we're doing. Any problems let me know.' George turns to the flight engineer, but is interrupted.

'Speedbird 200.' It is Departure Control. 'Do you require radar assistance?'

'Not at the moment,' George tells them. 'We're at 1,200 feet, visual over the water, and climbing — just! I'm turning now onto heading 280. Please watch us and warn if you think we're nearing high ground.' Then to his flight engineer, 'Right John, let's recap.'

'I've completed the fire drill on number one engine. The fire's out, I've shut down the number two engine. All secondary actions are complete. Hydraulics are all normal, but we're down to two generators. I've completed the drill and shed all unnecessary electrical loads. Can't see any other damage at the moment.'

'Good. We'll have to dump fuel. Can you calculate how much we need to dump to get down to landing weight, and how long it'll take?'

'Captain,' says the Cabin Services Director (CSD) hovering discreetly at the back of the cockpit. He hesitates to interrupt, but knows something needs to be said to calm the passengers.

A British Airways Boeing 747-236B in Landor livery.

'They're getting very anxious back there. Could you make an announcement as soon as possible?'

'Of course — but not right now. Tell 'em we've had an engine failure — we're flying safely — I'll explain what's happening in a few minutes.'

'Speedbird 200,' ATC interrupts again. 'Be advised fuel dumping is not permitted in your area. You'll have to climb to 10,000 feet and go out over sea.'

'Can't do that,' states George, calmly but firmly. 'Right now, I can hardly climb at all. If we don't dump, we'll never get to 5,000 feet, let alone 10,000, or even past these mountains. I'm way overweight for landing. We must dump fuel urgently. And if I try to turn, I think we'll start going downhill.'

'Skipper,' says John, 'we need to dump 55 tonnes. That'll take 30 minutes. When do you want me to start?'

'As soon as possible but, first, please go back into the cabin. Let me know what you can see. Look for any fire damage, holes in the engine cowls and wing, that sort of thing. And ask the

99

cabin crew if they saw anything. Meanwhile, I'll talk to the passengers. Brian, your R/T. Put her on autopilot and keep her climbing as best you can straight ahead. Just stay visual, parallel to the coast.'

The co-pilot engages the autopilot and selects heading mode. George collects his thoughts. If the crew are feeling rattled, the passengers must be really scared. He picks up the PA handset. 'Ladies and gentlemen, this is the captain. Please listen carefully. Despite the loud bangs you've all heard, we're flying safely and climbing out over the water. Unfortunately, we hit some birds on take-off and they have damaged an engine, but we still have sufficient power on the others. We'll be dumping some fuel to get down to landing weight. This will take about half an hour. Then we'll return to Vancouver. I know how alarmed you must be, but please rest assured, we have everything well under control. We're flying very nicely and it won't be long before you're all safely back on the ground.' George puts the handset down, thinking, Better not to tell them the whole truth just yet! 'So how did that go down?' he asks, as the CSD reappears in the cockpit.

'They seem a little happier,' comes the reply, 'but the ones at the back on the left side, by the windows, saw the fire and are very shaken.'

'I'm not surprised!' George says. 'For your ears only — we've lost two engines and are only just able to maintain height. We'll get back all right, but it won't be easy. Secure the cabin and brief the cabin crew for an emergency landing, but please do it discreetly. It'll be a good half hour before we can start an approach. I'll let you know when to brief the passengers for the landing, meanwhile keep them calm and let me know from time to time how they are. Oh — and also when I need to say some more calming words.'

George turns back to their immediate problems. Brian has everything under control on autopilot. They are nearly up to 1,500 feet and well clear of the high ground. There is solid cloud above, high ground on either side, and sea below — it's like flying through a wide letterbox slit. They have to keep visual and stay over the water to be certain of avoiding the nearby mountains.

John, who's gone back into the cabin to inspect the engines, returns and reports no obvious damage to the number one engine and no signs of fire. The cowling on number two is holed in several places but the wing looks OK. He sits down at the engineer's panel and rechecks his fuel dump calculations. 'OK, skipper. 55 tonnes it is. It'll take thirty minutes. Shall I start the fuel dumping checklist?'

'Yes. We won't *ask* ATC, I'll just *tell* them.' Normally, they would need to climb to at least 10,000 feet, ask permission to dump, and be directed to a suitable area. But in this situation, still below 2,000 feet and surrounded by mountains, there is no guarantee the two remaining engines are totally undamaged. It is best to get back on the ground as soon as they safely can.

John reads the checklist. 'OK to start?'

'Yes, I've told ATC — and told them we have to do it now.'

Gradually, as the fuel is pumped out and the aircraft weight reduced, they are able to climb and turn without losing height. They start a slow turn towards the southeast back over the water between Vancouver Island and the mainland. They tell ATC they are still visual and must remain so. They need to make long turns up and down the Strait over the water till down to landing weight. George also wants to stay within twenty miles of the airport in case they need to land in a hurry. ATC are very helpful and tell them all other traffic is being held well clear.

George picks up the PA. 'Ladies and gentlemen, this is the captain again. We've started dumping fuel to reduce the aircraft weight ready for landing. It will be some twenty minutes before we can start our approach. Those of you with window seats behind the wings will see fuel vapour pouring out from the dump pipes. This is normal and nothing to worry about. The cabin crew will now brief you about the precautions you need to take before we land. The details are very important, and I ask you please to pay close attention to them. We expect our landing to be entirely normal, but we still need everything ready just in case we have to evacuate the aircraft in a hurry.

Contemporary British Airways aircraft and uniforms.

A BOAC advertisement from the 1960s.

The airport is ready for our landing, and our ground staff are standing by to look after you when you leave the aircraft.' He hopes that was sufficiently reassuring, and they continue circling up and down over the water.

'Dumping complete, skipper,' says John. 'Ready for the top of descent and approach checklists?'

'Yes, please,' says George. 'But, first, let's do a briefing.' They discuss the safety heights (the heights they must achieve to remain safe above the high ground, most of which they are well below), the vital need to remain visual clear of the mountains, which runway to use, the radio navigation aids they need, and the procedure in case they have to go around for another approach. 'We'll ask for runway 26L. It's 11,500 feet long, more than enough. ATC have confirmed that all emergency services are ready.' Then he adds, 'OK, Brian, I'll take her now. I have control — thanks for minding the shop. Tell ATC we're ready to start an approach. We need vectors to give us at least a 10-mile final on the ILS for 26L.'

The radar controller gives them radar vectors (headings to steer) that take them well south around the airfield. Then he turns them northward to establish on a long final approach for the instrument landing system (ILS) that will give radio guidance down to the runway.

'Change now to Tower, one-one-eight point seven, they're all ready for you.' Brian changes frequency as instructed.

'Speedbird 200, Vancouver Tower. You're cleared to land runway 26L, wind 240 less than 10 knots. Emergency services are standing by halfway down the runway on the left side. They'll follow you down the last part of your landing roll. Confirm it's the number one and number two that have failed and please advise if you have any signs of fire.'

Brian confirms that all fire warnings have stopped and they expect a normal landing. George asks the fire services to inspect both engines on the left side after they land in case there is fire and they have to evacuate. He disengages the autopilot, lines the aircraft up on the approach, and asks for the landing checklist. With the wheels now down, he starts to descend towards the runway.

'You can wind the rudder trim out now, John,' George says. This done, he must again press hard on the right rudder pedal to balance the thrust from the good engines on the right side and keep the aircraft straight. He concentrates totally now on the runway ahead, making small power adjustments to control their speed and descent path.

As they come over the runway, about to touch down, a vehicle runs onto the runway and stops. What the hell is he up to! 'Standby to go around,' George calls, then, 'Go around, flaps 20.' He increases power on the good engines, raises the nose into a climb, and has to push even harder on the rudder pedal as the power comes on.

Brian moves the flap lever to the 20-degree position, then calls, 'Positive climb.'

'Gear up,' replies George, and they climb away. 'Tell 'em I want a left-hand circuit and get that ruddy vehicle clear!'

They climb slowly, turn left, level out at 1,500 feet and fly south around the airfield to attempt another landing. The crew have to go through the whole approach and landing procedure again, by which time George's right leg will be aching with fatigue!

They line up again ten miles out from the runway and make the long approach once more.

'One hundred above,' John calls out. 'Decide.'

'Land,' says George. As they come over the runway, he slowly reduces the engine power, eases the main wheels onto the ground, lowers the nose and calls for idle reverse on the operative engines, three and four.

When the 747 has slowed to taxi speed, he turns left off the runway onto the taxiway so that the damaged engines are downwind from the fuselage. The Fire Chief comes on the radio and confirms no sign of fire.

George breathes a huge sigh of relief, calls the CSD on the interphone and tells him they will be keeping the passengers on board. He knows an emergency evacuation always results in minor injuries.

A British Airways Boeing 747-200
in Landor livery.

He then turns to Brian, 'Ask ATC for a tug to tow us in.' He puts the parking brake on while they wait for it to be coupled up, picks up the PA and reassures the passengers that they are down safely. He thanks them all for remaining so calm and instructs them to remain seated while the aircraft is towed in.

But in the cockpit George sits bathed in sweat, it drips off his nose, it's in his eyes, his shirt is soaked. His right leg aches. He feels utterly limp. Gradually the tension eases. He grins weakly at his fellow crew members who are equally exhausted. Then he feels a hand on his shoulder.

'Well done, everyone. Good control of the aircraft, George, well managed emergency procedures.' It is the instructor. In reality, they are not in an aircraft at all. They are in a simulator at the airline's training centre. They have been on the ground the whole time. But the reality has been overwhelming. It was one of the regular training exercises that all crews undertake every six months to help them remain sharp, ready for the real thing — the genuine emergency.

The beer will taste extra good this evening.

Things You Hear at the Pub

It had been a while since I'd last seen my Aunt Margaret, not since before Uncle Henry died. Despite her being my aunt we're actually much of an age as my mother is so much older than her. She's an interesting woman, used to work as a nurse at one of the major hospitals in Exeter before she married Uncle Henry; now she's a barmaid at the Rose and Crown. I was looking forward to seeing her again in her new setting, she's such a keen observer of human nature.

I'd been been away sailing with John and Liz, we'd weathered a couple of storms in the Channel, but when a force nine was forecast we dcided to cut short our cruise and leave the boat safe in a marina in Plymouth. Many aviators are drawn to sailing, it has much in common with flying — the same respect for the elements, the same love of the vastness of the seas and skies. I had volunteered to drive down to check the mooring lines and decided to break my journey in Deddleigh. It's not far off the A38 before you reach Plymouth. I telephoned ahead, she was surprsied to hear from me and said to drop in soon after the lunchtime rush so there'd be time to talk.

The countryside around Deddleigh is a mixture of wooded hills and fields with cattle in the valleys. It's a sleepy little place, only about two hundred people; picture-book pretty in summer but wet and windy in winter. Deadly, the locals call it — old joke. As you come into the centre, the road splits into a Y before going down the hill to Deddmouth. In front of you, between the arms of the Y, is the village green, too small for cricket, and with a hump in the middle. To the left there's a church, and facing it across the green is the Rose and Crown, a low thatched building, separated from the road by a small lawn. As I opened the door of the pub I was nearly overwhelmed by the smells — wet dog, beer and tobacco, all overlaid with a good dose of Brasso. Someone must have been polishing the copper kettles and brasses I saw lining the window sills and mantelpiece in the saloon. There were two bars, public on the left, from which came the canine smells, and a cosy saloon on the right. Aunt Margaret waved from the serving area between them and greeted me with a peck on the cheek. 'Still got some clearing to do. What'll you have while you wait?'

'Just a sandwich and a coffee. I've got to be in Plymouth this afternoon.'

'I'm sorry you don't come down more often,' she said, wiping round the bar, 'You haven't been to this pub before, have you? What've you been up to all these years?'

Before I could answer, she was called over to the public bar to serve some locals. When she'd finished she came and sat with me. I asked her how this new life was treating her.

'Can't complain. Not so new now, it's over three years now, you know, since your Uncle Henry died. Never thought I'd be a barmaid. When he died, Mr Timms, he's the landlord, he asked if I'd like to help out, part-time like. He's a good sort, thought I might need the money, and the work would help take me out of myself, he said. It's very ordinary here but I like it.'

I finished my sandwich and asked for another coffee. I knew once she got going there'd be no stopping her. She finished polishing some glasses and poured me more coffee. 'Mr Timms runs a tight ship, used to be a senior steward in one of the big airlines, your lot I think, before he took the pub, before that he was on the Queens with Cunard.' she went on. 'But now, he presides over these two bars while Betsy, that's his wife, runs the small kitchen at the back. She makes the sandwiches, ploughman's and things — like what you're eating now — nothing fancy, just pub snacks. But it's a good place to work, and lots to do. Wasn't long before I became full-time. Mr Timms, now, he's a bit of a flatterer. He said when I started, the takings went up dramatically, but I think he's exaggerating. A real asset, he said and that's when he asked me to be full-time.'

I could see why — Aunt Margaret is in her mid-forties, and still very good looking. I guess Mr Timms made a very good business decision!

'The locals are alright. I've lived in Deddleigh most of my life,' she went on. 'Grew up here before I married your uncle. Know most of them well, knew 'em even before I started working behind the bar. You'd be amazed what you learn when you work in a pub. After a few drinks, voices rise — even the most intimate things are sometimes overheard. People don't realise what you can hear from behind the bar. There's a lot of gossip, I guess Mr Timms and I know most things that go on in the village, probably more than the doctor and certainly more than the vicar!

'Now, Old Fred, he does the hedges and ditches, cuts the village green and does odd jobs for the elderly, he knows a thing or two too. Doesn't say much, comes in for his pint each evening before going home but keeps his ears and eyes open. And he's good on the wildlife — animals, birds, plants and things, not just people's goings-on.' She lowered her voice and leant towards me. 'He once told me, "There's more goes on in this 'ere village be'ind closed doors than any of 'em dramas on telly. Young Mrs Knowles, 'er as lives down the lane on t'other side, she entertains the butcher — the one 'oo comes round with the van, *and* the boatman from Deddmouth, an' one or two others an' all, 'er husband being away so much up north."

'Vicar's a funny bloke too. Nice enough, but always dishevelled, threadbare collars, jacket cuffs all frayed and going through at the elbows. He teaches at the local school, he's a bachelor but not "one of those". There's talk, there always is, but I'm sure he's never touched a boy in his life, nor a woman for that matter. He very much needs to be taken in hand, and given a good shave too, always misses bits. Good at his job though, preaches short sermons I'm told, I never go to church, and he's always helping people in need. Comes in from time to time, drinks a pint or two, talks about the village and the school, never one to gossip though, he's always very careful about that.

'But the really queer one is the playwright.' And she lowered her voice again, 'I've never seen him, even though he lives in the old vicarage by the church, opposite. Poor vicar had to move out into a tiny bungalow when the vicarage was sold. Well, I'll tell you, the playwright, he's very odd, lives there with his mother and anorexic wife — she looks anorexic, needs a good feed, that's for sure. People say he doesn't look too good either, ever so pale and drawn as if he never goes out of doors, and when he is seen, which isn't often, always in dressing gown and slippers. They say his play, the only one that's ever been successful, is all about incest and murder. Makes one wonder what really does happen behind those closed doors.'

There was a shout of, 'Oi, Maggie, bloke's dyin' of thirst over 'ere.' She got up to serve the two locals over in the other bar.

'When those village lads come in,' she continued, rattling on in the way I remembered so well, 'it gets a bit noisy but they're good humoured most of the time. The usual mix: farm workers, two boys who've left school and supposed to be looking for work, a layabout who never does a thing, the carpenter's mate and the young mechanic who works for George at the garage. He can fix anything — cars, farm machinery, boats, even washing machines, fridges and the like. Also, the boatman, the one from down by the river, the one Old Fred thinks is seeing Mrs Knowles. They never get too rowdy though, I think that's because Mr Timms knows how to keep order without being too bossy.

'The tourists in summer usually sit outside, mum and dad, the kids and the dog. There's benches and tables, and a water bowl for dogs. They don't usually stay long, either on their way down to the coast or taking a breather after a day on the beach. We find the odd bucket and spade left behind with slimy sea creatures trying to clamber out. Often wonder whether dad does it on purpose so's they don't slop out in the car.

'When winter comes, of course, we only have the locals. It's the same year after year. I'm usually alone in the bar at lunchtime when it's quiet. We still get the odd stranger, but not often. Occasionally someone interesting comes in. Now, you'll never believe all this. Few years ago, a very nice young bloke — well, I say young, probably early thirties — dropped in and ordered a cider, and a bacon sandwich. Though I say it myself, our bacon sandwiches are the best, the bacon comes from Harry, the butcher down the village, he makes his own, and Betsy always makes sure there's lots of rashers in her sandwiches. This young bloke, he polishes off his sandwich and his cider and asks for another. "Famished," he says, "never had such good bacon before." The saloon bar was empty, only him, and the public bar with the two lads who's supposed to be looking for work, not that they seem to do much of that, far as I can see. Well, this nice young bloke, while he's waiting for his second sandwich, says he's looking for somewhere to rent, do I know of anything?

'"Well," I tells him, "I know for a fact there's lots of spare room at the old vicarage, and there's a cottage going begging." So I tell him about the playwright, and said I was sure he'd not want to be near him. "But you could try the village shop, there's a board inside the door with small notices; might be something there. And there's an annex at Mr Luscombe's farm, about a mile down the road towards Deddmouth, he's looking for a tenant." So he asks directions to the farm, enjoys his second sandwich, says he'll go and look. And that's all I heard for a while.

'Now, Mr Luscombe's a large tweedy gent with a florid face. Has a dairy farm, large for the area, with meadows that go down to the river. Drops by occasionally for a whisky or two. "Maggie!" Always a bit loud he is. "You got a moment? Young fellah came by the other day, wants to rent my annex. Says you told him. Now, you're a good judge of character, what d'you think of him?"

'"Never seen him before," says I. "Said he was in the airlines," says loud Mr Luscombe, "seems too young to retire," and I tell him I'd rather taken a liking to him. Julian, his name was. Anyways, to cut a long story short, he rented the place and came back to the pub to thank me. It was in the evening, we were busy so no time to chat, said he'd come back next day and tell me about it. It being winter, with no one around at lunchtime, just him, we soon began to chat. He came in regular like after that, not every day, just two or three times a week — for a cider and a sandwich. Gradually, I learnt more about him. Hadn't really wanted to go flying, father had been a captain, but as his eyesight had let him down he became a steward instead. Said it was OK at first, but didn't really like being away so much, so left. Now he was re-thinking his life, wondering what to do.

'Seemed a bit lost to me. Really nice bloke, I thought, rather delicate looking in a refined sort of way, well-spoken, interested in arts and things. Mr Timms isn't like that at all. You can see he's been around a bit. Unlike Julien. One evening, he got very tiddly, Julian I mean — nothing unruly just sentimental and sad. Didn't want to leave at closing time, said he'd nothing to go home to. I fear I broke one of my golden rules, and Mr Timms's too — never take a customer home, but I took him back to my place for a coffee. He needed to sober up, being in no fit state to drive down the hill. I knew he wouldn't try anything on — not that sort. But I took care not to let the locals see. Didn't want any of the usual gossip.

'When we got in, I sat him down on the sofa and went into the kitchen to make the coffee, but when I came back, he was fast asleep, just like a baby he was. So I drank the coffee while he snored. He must have been dreaming about something, he rolled around, nearly fell off and kept clutching a cushion. After midnight, he suddenly woke up. Looked distraught, surely he wasn't going to cry.'

Aunt Margaret lowered her voice to a whisper. I leaned forward to hear. 'Then he says, "I have to tell you something — something I've never told anyone else before — ever." Whatever's he going to say, I thinks. Then he looks round the room, everywhere else, 'cept me, takes his time. "I want to be a woman." To say I was surprised — well — I just sat there, I mean what do you say? "Are you really sure?" "Yes, yes," he says and starts to ramble on — 'bout his childhood, being an only boy, joining the airline, not fitting in, not really knowing who he was. All a bit garbled. Then he quieted down and told me how difficult it was to be a woman in a man's body. He'd known he was not a real man from when he was thirteen, puberty — you know — didn't like the way his body was developing, nothing he could do, just had to make the best of a bad job. But now, twenty years on, he'd chucked his job and wanted to change — but how?

'There wasn't much I could say. I made sympathetic noises, gave him some rugs and said to sleep on the sofa, I had to go up to bed, or I'd be late for work in the morning. When I came down, he'd gone. Left a nice little thank you note, he did, on the dining table. I didn't know what to do, I'd never heard anything like it before. I mean — lots of strange things happen in a small village, but never anything like that. I hummed and hawed, and in the end decided to confide in Mr Timms. It was a good thing I did 'cause he'd seen me go off with Julian and was wondering what he should say. He didn't say much, but I did go home happier that evening having shared the problem.

"'Have to go to Exeter tomorrow," he says next day, "You and Betsy can mind the pub, it being winter and quiet like." Julian didn't come in for his usual, only Old Fred and one or two locals in the evening. I didn't see Mr Timms again until the day after. "Here," he says, slipping me an envelope, "Give this to Julian when you next see him. It's from a trick cyclist I know, don't tell him I gave it you, say it was the doctor or something."'

"'Was that why you went up to Exeter?" "Yes," he says, and went on doing the accounts. Well, when Julian came in several weeks later, I slipped him the note saying I'd asked the doctor about what he'd said, but without letting on, and he'd recommended this bloke who was a specialist in problems like his. Julian looked horrified I'd spoken to anyone, but I assured him I'd not betrayed his secret. I never saw Julian again. Years later, when Mr Timms was taking his afternoon nap, he does these days, a couple comes into the saloon bar. The gent orders a beer and some sandwiches and a tonic with ice and lemon for the lady and they sit quietly in the corner while I gets on with the glasses so's to be ready for the evening. When they'd finished, he asks for the toilets, the lady gets up too, I thought to do the same, but then she comes over and says quietly, "Do you know who I am?" "No," says I. "I'm Julian, but I'm called Julie now. Thanks for the advice you gave me, it all worked out. I've had the op and now I've a job with an airline again. They've based me at Exeter where I can make a new start." She shuts up when the gent comes back, well I suppose it was her boyfriend, you never know these days, and they left. Drove off down to Deddmouth, they did.

'I told Mr Timms that evening, in private. All he said was, "When you've been in the airlines as long as I was, you get to know a thing or too, bit like the pub!"'

Someone was Holding my Hand

'Yes, I knew him well — and his wife. I was at school with him.'

Malt whisky, candlelight, cigars, a good dinner, and five men around the table after the ladies had withdrawn. The conversation had been rather more stimulating than usual — Iraq, the Falklands War, did military interventions ever do any good? Some hospital stories (de-identified of course) from the medics, and a fund of intriguing insights into human foibles from our host, the judge, told with wit and relish. He was long retired having served in the High Court, and liked the old-fashioned ways. The others were still working: a surgeon in a big hospital near Heathrow, a local doctor (not mine but a good friend) who had worked in Africa before settling into a quiet country practice near Beaconsfield, a businessman, I can't remember what in, but also a town councillor, a solicitor in a well-known London firm, and me, a pilot with British Airways. Our wives were women to be reckoned with too. The surgeon's wife taught classics at a leading girls' school, the doctor's was an investigative journalist for a national newspaper, the town councillor's was a vet, though rather too full of the importance of her husband's position, and the solicitor's wife worked with mine on various charities.

The conversation had drifted onto the difference between accidents and negligence. Had Maggie's government been negligent in not foreseeing Argentina's invasion of the Falklands? When might a surgeon be deemed negligent if a patient died? Was the council negligent in not erecting notices near a weir before a small boy fell in and drowned? When should individuals exercise common sense to avoid obvious danger? What is obvious and what is not?

The judge lowered his glasses and quietly maintained, 'An accident is an incident that no one could reasonably have foreseen and for which no one should be held responsible.' And he went on, 'Whereas negligence is when a person's acts or omissions could reasonably have been foreseen to be likely to cause injury.'

'But that,' I said, 'begs the question, what is reasonable?'

'You're in the risk business,' blustered the councillor. 'What about that crash in Scotland a few years back? The one where so many people were killed. The pilot survived, didn't he? Surely he must have known he was at fault. The papers certainly thought so.'

'Not necessarily,' I countered. 'He'd taken every possible precaution. He blamed himself, of course, but that doesn't imply guilt.'

'Well he bloody well shouldn't have tried to take-off when he did.'

'Do you know all the circumstances? Have you read the accident report?'

'I read the newspapers. At the very least, I think he was foolhardy...'

But before he could continue, the surgeon said, 'I deal with life and death decisions all the time. I know it isn't easy. However hard you try, you can't always foresee every complication. Take the case where you've carried out all the right procedures, you've exercised all your professional skills, you've followed all the rules, yet still something goes wrong and the patient dies. Perhaps another surgeon does things slightly differently and the patient lives. What was different — the procedures, the skills, something about the patient's condition or what? Who's right, who's wrong?'

'Or was it malpractice, negligence, a genuine mistake — or — totally unforeseen circumstances?' added the judge. 'It's a sliding scale, sometimes exceedingly difficult to differentiate. Of course, a surgeon or a pilot has a duty of care for which the law requires a higher standard than for the layman. But what's your opinion — as a professional pilot?'

'Bear with me and I'll try to explain,' I said. 'It's an interesting story with some strange twists. Not only from the aviation point of view, but some medical aspects too.'

And so I started. 'When Adrian left school, he joined the RAF, did seven years I think before joining British North Atlantic Airways. By all accounts he was a good pilot and the Boeing 707 was well maintained. You can find all that in the accident report. BNAA have a good record and Adrian was a cautious man — a real professional.'

'But the papers said he'd failed a flying test, a check flight or something. They made quite a song and dance of it at the time. Was that relevant?' asked the solicitor.

'I wouldn't think so,' I replied, 'it happened years ago, long before the accident.'

'But surely it shows a weakness of some kind?'

'Possibly, but more usually it's just a minor technicality. He was a good pilot, most of us have failed a test at some time or another, I know I have. I'm sure it wasn't a factor in the accident.'

I paused, thinking how best to explain. Laying a fork on the table, I started by showing the effect of a crosswind. 'On the ground, an aircraft is rather like a weathercock, if a strong wind blows from the side, it wants to turn into wind.' I pushed the tines of the fork to show the wind pushing on the rudder from one side. 'Every aircraft type has a defined crosswind limit. If the wind speed is below it, the pilot can keep the aircraft straight; if it is stronger, he runs the risk of being blown off the runway. During the flight testing of every new type of aircraft, the test pilots must demonstrate that this limit is safe. In fact, there's always a little leeway as it's set slightly below the maximum demonstrated speed which, in turn, is usually lower than the maximum crosswind the aircraft can sustain. All this has to be proven to the satisfaction of the Civil Aviation Authority — it allows for average piloting ability and

The flight deck of a Boeing 707.

various operational contingencies. With me so far?'

'So you're saying it's not the absolute speed limit?' asked the doctor.

'No, it isn't. But every pilot treats it as such. For example, the wind hardly ever blows consistently, there are gusts and eddies, measurements on the day are not always accurate, things like that — the margin is there to allow for this.'

'But this chap took off when the wind was too strong, it's obvious, it was in *The Times*,' said the councillor.

'Ah, but have you ever known newspapers to be totally accurate?' observed the solicitor. 'My firm deals mainly with financial disputes, frequently I find things misrepresented by the media.'

'Agreed, but let's get back to the story,' I said. 'I saw a lot of Adrian after the accident, he lived near me. He was totally devastated by it, not only had he been badly injured but he felt so horribly responsible. The AAIB, that's the Air Accident Investigation Branch, took a long time to publish its findings;

in fact they didn't do so until after he died. And throughout that time, his airline kept him dangling on a string. Even though the doctors had passed him fit again and his flying licence had been renewed, they wouldn't let him fly. He just remained in limbo, his managers didn't have the balls to make a decision. They just hid behind the AAIB report.'

'That's understandable,' said the judge, 'No airline would wish to be seen employing someone who might be guilty of negligence.'

'But the point is this — he was never guilty of anything. The AAIB is an independent body, they don't apportion blame. It isn't like a court of law or even a tribunal. It only determines causes and makes recommendations to improve safety. No one found him guilty, neither then nor afterwards.'

'But he still killed a lot of people,' added the councillor. 'Someone has to answer for that.'

'No, he didn't kill anyone, it was an accident. The report has a detailed account of how very carefully he checked everything. The flight planners confirmed he checked the weather with them, and the ATC tape proves that he kept checking the wind speed right up until the start of the take-off roll. The wind was gusting up and down, sometimes above the crosswind limit of the aircraft, so he waited prudently until the wind dropped. It's all on the record. When he started the take-off, the wind was below the limit. It was safe. But unfortunately, during the take-off roll, it suddenly increased; Adrian was unable to keep the aircraft straight. As you know, it went off the side of the runway and hit another aircraft.'

'But surely every pilot knows the wind varies and forecasts are unreliable?'

'Yes, we do, but this wasn't a forecast — it was a series of reported measurements from the anemometer on the airport control tower.'

'OK, but why didn't he stop when he saw he was being blown towards the side of the runway?'

'That was because it happened after V1. V1 is the decision speed we always calculate for every take-off. After that speed, you are committed to take-off because there isn't room to stop. If you try, you'll go off the end of the runway. And you must remember it all happened so fast. He did his best to get airborne, but failed by a whisker.'

'So what were the mitigating circumstances?' asked the judge. 'You maintain he wasn't negligent but there must be some factors that weren't taken into account or there wouldn't have been an accident. If he wasn't to blame, who was?'

'The AAIB confirmed that the aircraft had been operated correctly, but they pointed out that the anemometer on the control tower was some way from where the aircraft went off the runway.' Again, I arranged things on the table to illustrate the layout of Prestwick airport, the direction of the runway towards the northwest, the wind blowing off the sea from the southwest, the control tower at the southeast end of the runway, over a mile from where the aircraft crashed, and the fact that the accident site was nearer the sea than the control tower. 'The AAIB,' I continued, 'did detailed calculations and determined that the wind had suddenly and unexpectedly strengthened. It was much stronger where the accident happened than where it was measured at the control tower.'

'So was the design of the airport faulty?' asked the solicitor.

'Difficult to say. It'd been used for many years — certainly since the war — without this problem having occurred before,' I replied. 'But they did make a recommendation that an additional anemometer at the northern end of the runway, nearer the sea, would be advisable.'

'Another factor, of course, was the taxiway running along so close beside the runway,' commented the judge. 'I would question whether airports should be designed like that.'

'But nearly all airports throughout the world are designed like that, there's nothing unusual about Prestwick. To my mind, it was just a tragic set of circumstances. Sheer happenstance that the other aircraft was there. In your words, "an incident which no one could reasonably have foreseen and for which no one should be held responsible,"' I answered.

'But you can't just leave it like that,' said the councillor.

'Someone has to be to blame for all those deaths and all that misery.'

'That's as maybe,' I countered. 'But the blame game can inhibit finding the truth. The legal process doesn't always improve air safety. It's far more important to learn exactly what occurred and to prevent it happening again. But you're right about the misery — well over a hundred families devastated, so many lives shattered, two airlines in shock. I've seen it at close hand, I know what it's like. Remember it was one of our aircraft it hit and Adrian was a good friend. The vital thing is to learn so it never — ever — happens again.'

'Perhaps you are too close to it.'

'Yes, I probably am. When I visited Adrian in hospital, he was miserable. You see — he felt so responsible despite the fact he'd checked everything so carefully. He told me all he could remember — his concern about the wind; the take-off being normal until just after V1; then drifting towards the edge of

The flight deck of a VC10.

the runway; trying desperately to keep it straight; knowing he couldn't stop; doing his best to get into the air. Then, when it went onto the grass, slamming the throttles shut and braking hard.

He said the ghastly sight of the other aircraft filling his windscreen would haunt him forever. Then the crash — and nothing.'

There was silence round the table. 'And there's something else.' Even though I was among friends, still I hesitated. 'I don't know what you think of near-death experiences, but this is what he told me. I'd never heard of them before, it was the first time I'd heard someone talk about it. I'll try and tell you what he said in his own words. He said, "Everything was silent. Total darkness. That was all. Nothing else. I couldn't see, I couldn't hear, I wasn't cold, I wasn't hot, just blissfully warm and comfortable, floating in some indefinable space. I knew something bad had happened, but there was no pain. Then, far out in the velvet blackness, I saw a bright light. White, beautiful, pure, soft, and so welcoming. I drifted slowly towards it along a black velvet tunnel. Someone was holding my hand.

The flight deck of a Boeing 747.

I felt serene. Surrounded by love. I knew I was dying, but I wasn't frightened. Everything felt so right, so peaceful — I was being welcomed into a place more beautiful than anywhere I'd ever been before. I was being led towards it. I followed gladly. If this was dying, I wanted to die — it was wonderful."

'He said it was so beautiful he couldn't find words to describe it. He didn't think anyone would believe him. I was the only person he'd told. Then he said he felt someone pounding his chest, he heard voices saying they thought he'd gone. He wished he had — but where? He felt as though a whole rugger scrum was trampling him underfoot. He said his body ached all over — but his inner being ached even more, hoping to return to the serenity of that white space. Then, there were more voices, a warm feeling and everything disappeared.

'Next, he could smell burnt meat, kerosene and fresh cut grass. He became aware of his face being pressed into muddy ground, and not being able to breathe. There was a diesel engine roaring nearby. Red flames were crackling overhead. Someone was shouting, "Over here! Over here!" Then blackness. Silence.'

'I've heard similar things at the hospital,' said the surgeon. 'Some say it's a religious experience but, personally, I think the white light is a physiological reaction to lack of oxygen in the brain, I don't think there's anything mystical about it.'

'I'm not so sure,' interrupted the doctor. 'I've seen some very strange things in Nigeria, not juju but definitely verging on the metaphysical — very difficult to explain.'

'But that's not the end of it,' I added. 'He said it altered his whole perception of death, it no longer frightened him. When he left hospital, his life was made a misery; he was pilloried in the press, the paparazzi besieged his house — you know his wife couldn't even go shopping without being followed by reporters. Naturally, the accident investigators asked probing questions, his neighbours shunned him, and even his friends began to doubt him. As for his airline, the management conducted an internal company inquiry which left him stunned and isolated — they didn't actually blame him because they couldn't find any evidence to support that judgement. Even when he was fully recovered, they wouldn't let him go back to flying; instead they asked for his resignation. I saw him frequently and watched him becoming more and more depressed. I think he saw death as an easy way out.'

'Did he seek medical help?'

'No, I don't think he trusted anyone any more. This went on for months. I watched him decline, he began to talk of death as a friend. He said he wished he'd died in the accident, that bright light had been so comforting and peaceful.'

'I've studied this a bit,' said the doctor. 'The literature says NDEs — that's near-death experiences — can alter a person's whole life. Even, on some occasions, leading to marriage break-ups — I'm not sure why — but never to suicide.'

'I think his wife, who'd been very supportive, was at the end of her tether towards the end. It was nearly a year after the accident when she phoned me in a panic, she'd come home to find the garage door locked and the car inside with the engine running. She could see Adrian in the car, but wasn't strong

The flight engineer's panel of a VC10.

enough to break in, could I rush round and get him out. I said to call 999, I'd be there in a couple of minutes. I broke in through the window and dragged him out into the open air.

'He was barely conscious, had difficulty breathing. I didn't know what to do other than get him into the fresh air and comfort him, hoping the ambulance would arrive soon. We propped him up on some cushions, he looked so peaceful and, apart from his breathing, serene and healthy — "in the pink" you might say. He kept whispering it was so beautiful, he wanted to go to that exquisite place he'd seen before.'

'You did the right thing,' said the doctor. 'A classic case of carbon monoxide poisoning.'

'The ambulance arrived too late. His last words were, "Someone is holding my hand."'

I stopped. The memory of that scene still affected me greatly. The judge leant across and topped up my whisky.

'Thanks. He was such a very good friend; we'd known each other since childhood. Even now, I still keep thinking it could so easily have been me — I would have made exactly the same decisions. The margin between success and failure is so very small. Right to the end, he remained convinced he'd done nothing wrong; the world is so unfair.' I took a sip of my whisky, looked round the table and added, 'Why do people always want someone to blame?'

'Perhaps because life is so fragile,' said the surgeon. 'People don't like uncertainty, they can't accept it — but — sometimes accidents just happen.'

'I only hope he found that beautiful place.'

A Rum do

As my eyes adjusted to the gloom after the tropical glare outside, I saw again the familiar wooden panelling, the leaf-shaped punkahs in the ceiling, the rattan chairs and the old clock behind the bar. Brian was sitting in the far corner from where he could watch the main entrance.

Raising an imaginary glass, he caught the barman's eye as I came in. I gave an answering thumbs up and threaded my way past a group of boisterous Australians.

'I retreated over here so we could hear ourselves talk.'

The waiter brought us two ice-cold Tigers, the glasses beaded with moisture. 'The old place is not quite the same since the renovations,' I remarked. 'D'you remember how run down it all was? No air conditioning, shabby paint, rather dusty. I could so easily imagine Somerset Maugham sitting quietly in a corner observing the goings-on.'

'Your trouble is you're an old romantic,' said Brian. He downed some beer. 'Aaaah! That's good, I needed that. You know, it's good to see you again after all this time.'

We were in the Long Bar of the Raffles Hotel in Singapore. I wondered how many noisy events there'd been in this famous old hotel over the years: planters downing stengahs, businessmen escaping for sundowners at six, rowdy parties, glamorous dinner dances late into the night — all brought to a sudden stop by the invading Japanese. Now, it was full of rich tourists trying to glimpse a faded colonial past.

In the early 1960s, BOAC crews used to stay at the Raffles between flights. We had agreed to meet here to remind ourselves of how it had been when we were still new to the flying game. Exploring the world had been such an exciting adventure, and Singapore a mysterious, grubby, smelly, wonderful place. The noise and hubbub in the streets had not changed much, but gone were most of the low, white-painted buildings with red pantile roofs, replaced now by the high-rise, ultra-clean skyscrapers of a modern city. Even the old Raffles had been thoroughly refurbished and modernised.

We had first met when training, over twenty-five years ago. Although we went to different fleets, he to 707s, me to VC10s, we had remained good friends, meeting occasionally down the routes when our separate itineraries crossed. Now we were both on 747s, chance bringing us together once more. I was going on to Sydney the next day, he would be returning to London. That's what airline life is like.

We sipped our beers and told each other our small adventures since we'd last met — nothing spectacular, just things we'd seen, places we'd visited, old acquaintances bumped into, and the inevitable flying chat that pilots call 'opening the hangar doors'. Our careers had taken rather different paths. I liked the itinerant life down the routes and was happy to remain a line pilot, whereas he'd become a training captain. I hoped this hadn't changed him too much. He'd always been more serious than me, and I was relieved to see he had retained his sense of fun and love of flying.

I wanted to ask him about the affair in Trinidad. I'd heard the rumours and was hoping to find out from the man himself. However, when I broached the subject, he remained silent, staring into his near empty glass.

Suddenly, an enormous flash and a bang brought sheets of rain and chairs blew across the veranda. The sun went out. The bar fell quiet as everyone peered at the chaos outside. Waiters rushed to close windows. A table went flying.

'What a waste of good beer.'

'Just the usual afternoon thunderstorm,' I replied. 'I think we may be here some time. Fancy another?' I caught the barman's eye and motioned for more beer. 'Don't know about you, but I find thunderstorms rather fun.'

'Except when you're in 'em.'

'You're right. I remember one night some years ago. We were in a VC10 from Colombo to Singapore. Flying alongside the biggest row of thunderstorms I've ever seen. They towered above us almost the whole way to Sumatra. The lightning was continuous — amazing purple, white and brown ribbons — inside the clouds, between them and down to the sea. They even lit up the waves below. I've never seen anything like it. Fortunately, our track was well to the south in clear air. We had a smooth ride, so I just enjoyed the view.'

'You were lucky. I remember a night when we had to keep dodging between them. It really became "quite interesting" for a while. Hail and turbulence as well as lightning.'

I took another sip of beer and continued. 'Well, in the midst of all this, the steward came up to say the Anglican bishop of Singapore was on board, he'd like to see the cockpit. I agreed, of course. I like showing passengers what we do, and the chance to show a man of the cloth the wonders of the firmament seemed too good to miss. When he arrived, I showed him into the jump seat and pointed out the lightning on our left. He was genuinely interested, asking a great many perceptive questions

Piarco Airport in Trinidad.

about flying near thunderstorms.

'Then the St Elmo's fire started, great purple streaks flickering right across the windscreen. But something else happened too, something I'd never seen before — or since. A vast cone of purple light spread out into infinity in front of us. I couldn't help pointing out it exactly matched the colour of his shirt below his dog collar. He laughed, saying perhaps it was a message.'

'Were you struck at all?' Brian asked. 'It usually happens after St Elmo's fire.'

'No, but I thought we might. I turned up the cockpit lighting. Explained to the bishop this was so we wouldn't be blinded by the flash. There'd be a loud bang, I said, but no real danger. We waited — nothing happened. The purple cone disappeared. The St Elmo's fire subsided. The bishop was fascinated.

'When he was leaving the cockpit, I remarked, "Well, thank God we weren't struck by lightning." "Perhaps that's because today I was closer to my boss," he joked.'

Brian relaxed as we discussed other strange things we'd seen and done over the years. 'I suppose you want me to tell you about Trinidad.' I nodded while he looked into the distance outside.

'It really was the weirdest thing that's ever happened to me. It's a long story. Shall we have another beer?'

When the barman brought the Tigers, he began. 'It happened last year. You couldn't dream it up if you tried.'

'Try me then.'

'Well, we'd had a day off and were due to go back to Barbados. An evening departure. Light load, most of the people joining in Barbados for the flight to London. We closed up as usual, started engines and taxied out. So far so good. There we were, slowly taxiing towards the runway, when Air Traffic Control told us to stop and hold our position. No explanation — nothing. We waited — still nothing. We asked for our airways clearance — still nothing, just "standby". Two arriving aircraft were put in the hold overhead with no explanation. They asked why the delay. When could they expect landing clearance? ATC just told them to standby.

'Next, I saw a Toyota jeep careering across the grass — chased by two police cars. It weaved down the taxiway straight towards us and disappeared down the right side of the aircraft. I wondered what the hell was happening. We felt a slight bump, the aircraft began to vibrate, and the fire bell went off — it was a fire warning on the number four engine. We shut it down and I called ATC to ask if they could see anything.'

'Did the warning go out?' I asked.

'Yes, almost immediately,' Brian continued. 'ATC was still being useless, they didn't even bother to reply. I was more than somewhat concerned because I didn't know what was happening. Had the jeep caused the fire? Was it a coincidence? If it was the jeep, how much damage might've been done?'

'I guess you were worried about having to start an evacuation.'

'Yes. I was just about to call the Cabin Service Director to see if he'd seen anything when I saw the jeep disappearing off towards the hangars out on my left. I told ATC, but they still weren't interested. I also told them we needed to return to the terminal, but all they said was, "standby".

'Suddenly, we saw emergency vehicles tearing towards us and going round behind the aircraft where we couldn't see 'em. At this point my alarm bells really started ringing. Why weren't we being told anything? Why was ATC stonewalling? Was it some kind of terrorist attack? You never know these days.'

I told Brian I hadn't heard anything about a terrorist attack. 'So what really happened?'

'Well — I knew some of the passengers must have seen the blue flashing lights outside. I used the PA to reassure them. A minor problem with one of the engines. You know the sort of thing. Needed to return to the terminal — not to worry. The emergency vehicles were only there as a normal precaution. I played it all down, though I was anything but reassured! I could see police cars and emergency vehicles rushing all over the place.'

'Did you call company frequency?'

'Yes. I spoke to the station officer and asked if he knew

anything. He said he didn't, but he'd try to find out. I told him we'd be coming back to the terminal, and to be ready to receive the passengers. We waited some more. Then he called back saying he'd had no joy, there were lots of sirens going off. He could see blue flashing lights over by the edge of the airfield and search lights sweeping around behind our aircraft. I asked ATC again for taxi instructions back to the terminal but they didn't answer. The aircraft overhead were asking how long the delay would be. One said he was now short of fuel and would have to divert soon. ATC didn't bother to answer him, so I got on the radio and told him what we could see — which wasn't much.'

Brian explained that he had sent his flight engineer down into the cabin to see if he could see any signs of damage to the engine or the wing, but there was nothing obvious, which was a relief. No evacuation would be necessary. He'd called Speedbird London on HF radio to tell Ops Control what was happening. If it really was some kind of terrorist attack, the sooner London knew the better. He had talked to the Duty Controller who said he'd contact the Head of Security and the Chief Pilot.

Brian waited some more. ATC were still being useless — they wouldn't tell him anything, they wouldn't let him taxi the aircraft and neither would they help the other aircraft holding overhead. Speedbird London had called back to tell him that Hugh, the Chief Pilot, was on the phone, connected by phone patch.

Brian grinned at me. 'I told him the aircraft was safe and brought him up to date. There really wasn't much Hugh could do, it was one o'clock in the morning his time, and he was in his pyjamas! We agreed the best thing was to taxi back to the terminal and get the passengers off as quickly as possible. He said I was the man on the spot. He really couldn't run an airline from his kitchen table, so he'd back me to the hilt. He'd be by the phone if I wanted him.'

Torrents of rain continued to fall outside. I looked at Brian and couldn't help laughing at the idea of the Chief Pilot trying to run an airline in his pyjamas. 'He's not such a bad sort,' I said.

Brian smiled and continued, 'Then something even stranger happened. I couldn't see much in the dark, but a man ran across the airfield towards us and disappeared under our nose. The number three engine suddenly surged, rapidly followed by a very anxious CSD bursting into the cockpit to say the stewardess sitting by door two right had seen a man being swallowed by an engine.'

'What — right into the engine? I mean, I mean was he sucked in?' I asked, aghast.

'Yes, she couldn't believe what she'd seen, it was horrible. The engine surged again so we had to shut that one down too. At this point I was really getting worried and feeling pretty bloody-minded too. I told ATC, regardless of what they said, I was taxiing back to the terminal. They objected strongly. I told them I would declare an emergency if they didn't bloody well agree.'

'I'd have told 'em to bugger off,' I said. 'What was it like taxiing with only two engines on one side?'

'Difficult, but fortunately we were fairly light. We got back OK and disembarked the passengers down the forward steps into the terminal building. It was dark so they couldn't see much — which was a good thing because when I inspected the engines with the flight engineer, blood was still dripping out and there were body parts in the intake. The number four wasn't in very good shape either. It was only then we realised it must've swallowed bits of the jeep. There were score marks along the bottom of the cowling and the fan blades were badly chipped and bent.'

By this time the passengers were all in the terminal. He didn't know how much they'd seen but the cabin crew were well aware of what had happened.

'You know how quickly rumours spread and get exaggerated,' he said. 'I thought it best to brief the passengers as soon as possible. I went into the terminal, quietened them down and did my best to explain what we thought had happened. It wasn't much, but the main thing — everyone was safe.

'I told them the aircraft couldn't go anywhere until the engines had been repaired. We were trying to sort out hotel accommodation. If they had any questions, I'd try to answer them. Yes — all their baggage was coming off. No — there'd been no danger. Was it true a man had been killed? Yes — but we didn't know why. When would there be another aircraft? I couldn't answer that but said I'd told London and was sure they'd arrange a relief aircraft as soon as possible. The best thing was for everyone to go to their hotels and wait for more information in the morning. By then we would know what was planned.'

It was soon well after midnight. Brian continued, 'When I went back out to the aircraft, the ground engineers wouldn't touch the number three engine until the body parts had been removed. At that stage, there was nothing more we could do. I said we'd discuss it again in the morning. In the bus, on the way back to the hotel, the crew was a bit subdued. I was feeling very tired so went straight to bed, but some of the boys and girls stayed up for a few drinks.'

I asked Brian who were the others on the crew. 'Colin Crowe was the co-pilot, Harry Reynolds the flight engineer. But wait till I tell you the rest of the story. They were truly wonderful.'

'D'you mean there's more? Surely the station staff dealt with it all. After all, they know the ropes there.'

He paused, collecting his thoughts — clearly, what he was about to say was not easy.

He stared into his beer. I waited.

'Next morning, you won't believe what happened. I phoned the airport to see what'd been arranged. They were in the middle of a teleconference with London. There was a big problem — a stalemate. The ground engineers wouldn't work on the engine until all the body parts had been removed. The police wanted statements from everyone before anything was touched. The only person they'd allow near the engine was the undertaker. The undertaker said he wouldn't because he wasn't an engineer. The police wanted the body parts so they could identify the victim. And the undertaker wouldn't touch the body parts because they were still in the engine! They were going nowhere fast.

'I listened for a while, then volunteered to go out to the airport to see if I could help. Hugh thanked me and said he wanted to talk to me before I left. He phoned back and asked me to find out exactly what was going on. The stories he was being told were very confusing. Everyone was going round in circles. He wanted the facts quickly; an aircraft stuck on the ground was very expensive. I rustled up Colin and Harry, and off we went.'

When the three of them arrived at the aircraft, everyone was standing around not knowing what to do next. No one had touched the engine with the mangled body in it — the stalemate hadn't changed. Groups of people were shouting at each other. The police were trying to take charge but knew nothing about aircraft. The undertaker sat in his hearse saying nothing.

Brian explained how he had talked to the various groups and decided something imaginative was needed. So he and the station manager went off to one side to hatch up a plan. They then drove across the airport to talk to the fire brigade. The Fire Chief listened politely but was very reluctant to intervene. Eventually he was persuaded to show them how to use the fire hoses.

They drove back to the aircraft, followed by the fire engine, to find everyone still standing around. Brian took Colin and Harry to one side and explained the plan. Harry went to see the engineers while the station manager talked to the police whose agreement was essential.

'What'd you decided to do?'

'Simple — hose the body out. I asked the fire brigade to turn on the pumps and Colin and I just hosed it out. Have you ever handled a fire hose going at full chat?' he asked.

'No.'

'Well, it needed the two of us to hold it. We squirted a few people 'til we got the hang of it — that was the only funny thing all day. Harry stood by the engine and showed us where to point the hose. Then bits and pieces started falling out —

an arm, a foot still in a shoe, bits of leg, torn clothing, a badly mangled torso, and lots of pink water. The head was the most difficult bit — it was jammed in the fan blades.' Brian stayed silent for a while. 'It was totally and utterly disgusting — and smelly.'

The undertaker, he said, picked up the pieces one by one and put them in a box for the police to take away and identify — it wasn't even a coffin, more like a cardboard box.

'After we'd thoroughly washed out the engine, we then had to persuade the ground engineers to inspect it for damage.'

'How ghastly,' I said. 'I'm not sure I could have done it. How did they inspect the engine? Presumably with a borescope.' A borescope is much like a medical endoscope, it has an eyepiece and glass optical fibres with lights and can be passed into the innards of an engine to inspect the workings.

'Yes, they did — but we had to stand over them. Even after all the blood had been thoroughly washed out, they were still very reluctant. Harry had to direct them. However, they didn't find any damage and agreed to test the engine later in the day. Obviously, nothing could be done to the number four but at least a three-engine ferry flight was now an option.

'I called Hugh and told him what we'd done. He was amazed and thanked me profusely. "Over and above the call of duty," he said. "You must all be shattered."

'I told him it had been horrible and we were feeling rather sick. It was the first time I'd seen a mangled body. I never want to see another. Back in the hotel, I had a long soak in a bath. I felt grubby and smelly, even though I'd never been near the body.'

Despite sitting here, comfortably in the Long Bar in Singapore on the other side of the world, Brian looked pale and visibly shaken. I asked him how the rest of the crew had taken it.

'Pretty well really, but then they hadn't seen the body bits.'

He picked up his glass, looked at it and put it down again. 'To tell the truth, I feel a bit sick again now, just thinking about it.'

I waited to let him compose himself.

'After my bath, I joined the others by the pool. They asked where I'd been but I spared them the details. The stewardess who'd seen the man being swallowed by the engine was still a bit distressed. The rest were fairly calm about it. They speculated on where we'd be sent next. No one particularly wanted to stay in Trinidad.

'I'd just ordered a much-needed beer,' Brian chuckled, 'when the barman said there was a phone call for me. It was Hugh saying they'd organised the three-engine ferry flight and he was on his way to Trinidad. But first he explained Ops Control wanted us to fly the relief aircraft back to London next morning. He'd said, no way — not until he'd spoken to me. He thought we needed a break. We could either fly it all the way back to London or only as far as Barbados where he'd give us a few days off. "A party is what you all need," he said, "and as a thank you present for saving the company so much money." He asked me to talk it over with the crew. Not unnaturally they all opted for the stop in Barbados.

'It was one hell of a party!' Brian said. 'Far too many rum punches, but it did us a world of good. It's surprising how things get to you. One or two of the cabin crew definitely needed to let their hair down. I wasn't exactly a hundred percent, but Harry was the one most affected. He'd been the one who'd inspected the engine to see which bits needed washing out. It was he who'd persuaded the ground engineers to work on the engine. And — he'd helped the undertaker find all the bits. He was the real hero. Even though he was a tough ex-navy engineer, he'd found it very upsetting.'

'I'm not surprised,' I exclaimed. 'I've only had to deal with a couple of dead bodies. Heart attacks on aircraft — no blood or anything like that, but even that gave me a turn. Harry must have found it pretty gruesome. Did you ever find out why it happened?'

'Not really. About a month later Hugh phoned and told me all he knew. An American, on holiday with his boyfriend, was sharing a room in a small hotel near the airfield. They'd sunk most of a bottle of rum. There'd been a lovers' tiff or something, the American had struck the other man on the head with a fire extinguisher and thought he'd killed him. It seems he panicked, rushed out of the hotel, jumped into his hired jeep, driven down the road, crashed through the boundary fence out onto the airfield. No one knew why he'd driven into the aircraft and then climbed into the engine. In the end, the police had treated it as suicide. The party had been exactly what we'd needed.'

The thunderstorm was passing, the rain had eased, the streets outside were steaming in the sun. A torrent of water was rushing along the storm drains beside the road. We sat, watching the people picking their way between the puddles.

Brian finished his beer. 'I've often wondered about it since. He must have been desperate. Was he drunk, was it grief, remorse, or just plain panic? Why'd he driven all around the airfield like a maniac? In the dark it's a very confusing place; he was probably lost, may well have been dazzled by the aircraft's lights. Was that why he drove into the engine, was it deliberate or was it an accident? Or was he simply out of his mind?'

He was silent for a while before continuing, 'When the jeep had hit the engine, the main part had gone underneath, but some of the top had been swallowed in a shower of sparks. He hadn't been killed, though he must have been injured; there was blood all over the jeep. He'd managed to drive it away into one of the hangars on the far side of the airfield, where he'd left it. The police had been able to follow the trail of blood around the hangar and out onto the airfield again. He must have been very determined to have another go.'

Brian thought it must have been intentional. The stewardess had seen him walk very slowly and very deliberately towards the engine before reaching up to the intake and being sucked in.

'And what about the boyfriend?' I asked.

'I've no idea, it was a rum do,' he mused. 'I wonder what your bishop would've thought of it all.'

Suddenly, over Calgary

It is said that the cockpit of a Boeing 747 contains 971 controls, dials, switches and indicators. Hamish Reid took quiet pride in the fact that he knew every single one of them. A meticulous, even pedantic, pilot, he was extremely careful over all aspects of his flying, leaving nothing to chance. This, perhaps, was his saving grace because he could be a little careless of other people's feelings. He was respected rather than liked, and he respected only hard facts. There was little poetry in his soul.

As he climbed briskly up the circular staircase to the upper deck, he noted with approval the ordered activity around him. He entered the cockpit, examined the technical log, satisfied himself that the aircraft was fully serviceable, carefully placed his briefcase where he could reach it and settled himself into the captain's seat. Then, strictly in accordance with the manual, he carried out his pre-flight checks, arranged his maps and charts in the order in which he intended to use them, set the navigation aids as required for take-off and waited for the co-pilot to do the same on his side.

In his long career, he had flown over a dozen different types of aircraft, but the mighty Boeing was by far the best. He was impressed by its huge technical advance over the primitive machines he had first flown. In his early days, engine failures were a frequent curse; on jets they were a rarity. Propeller aircraft had been noisy and uncomfortable, whereas the 747 was serenely smooth. Its systems were extremely reliable, but not only that, if anything did fail, there were multiple back-ups. Flying had become almost too easy. During the war, he and his colleagues had been through fire, some literally, merely learning how to survive. He was proud of that.

Although, at first, deeply suspicious of the new pilots fresh from flying college, time was proving him wrong; many had even gained their commands. He was impressed by the way the young man beside him had flown the aircraft out to Los Angeles. This evening, it was Hamish's turn to fly the leg back to London. It would be a long fight, some ten hours or so, almost due north to the Canadian border, then up over Hudson Bay, Baffin Island, Greenland, Iceland, and finally down the length of the British Isles to Heathrow. He was looking forward to it, the weather forecast was excellent — not a cloud in the sky.

The sun was low on the horizon as the last passengers came on board. The aircraft, heavily laden with fuel for the long flight to London, was close to its maximum take-off weight. Before starting the engines, they ran through the procedures for stopping or continuing should an engine fail during take-off; noted the safety altitudes for each leg over the Rockies; and agreed the actions to be taken if anything prevented them from climbing past the mountains. All normal routine for cautious aviators.

They started up, taxied out to join the queue of departing aircraft and awaited their turn. Then, from ATC, 'Speedbird 282 heavy, wind 260 at 10, runway 25 right, cleared for take-off.'

Hamish aligned the aircraft precisely on the runway centre line, paused, opened up the power on the four Rolls-Royce engines, and began the take-off roll. Fifty-five seconds later they lifted off the runway and headed out to sea before turning back towards the coastline exactly as per the departure clearance.

During the long turn back towards the east, Hamish could see the lights of Los Angeles twinkling ahead, with multiple ribbons of red and white lights from traffic on the freeways. Back over the coast, they turned north-east towards the mountains, the lights thinning as they neared the foothills. The engines hummed quietly in the background, the air hissed past the windscreen, the instruments glowed softly around them, the co-pilot made routine radio calls, the flight engineer monitored the aircraft systems, and Hamish concentrated on

143

The city of Calgary in Alberta.

ensuring they would cross the mountains with height to spare.

After 35 years in aviation he knew how important it was to be cautious when flying towards high ground. You had to be ready for anything that might reduce the climb rate. Any inability to reach each designated safety altitude would require an immediate turn back. Wind speed and direction needed to be constantly checked — strong winds over mountains almost always cause turbulence. After flying for so many years, such things had become an ingrained habit — a matter of routine. But on that night, everything was absolutely normal. The engines continued their reassuring hum, all the systems were working normally, and there was not a cloud in the sky. It was 'gin clear'. He could see for miles; the air was silky smooth. It was a perfect night for flying.

After 30 minutes, they levelled out at 31,000 feet and continued northward over Nevada. The sun had disappeared in the western sky, leaving only a thin bronze glow along the horizon. The lights of Los Angeles were now far behind. Above, the stars were beginning to fill the sky. The Pole Star hung low ahead, guiding them northwards. In the dark of the night, they hardly needed the expensive navigation kit that modern aircraft now carry to know which way to go.

Soon, the distant lights of Spokane passed by far out to the west. They left US airspace, changed radio frequency, and contacted the Canadian controllers ahead. They were given a slight change of route, to take them past Churchill on the west coast of Hudson Bay, and were cleared to climb to 33,000 feet. Hamish reprogrammed the navigation system with the new waypoints which would now take them across Canada well to the south of their original plan. No matter. It was a bit disappointing, though, since he had been hoping to see the Northern Lights. The further south they flew, the less likely he would be to see them.

Continuing northwards, they had only the stars above to accompany them. Despite the excellent visibility, hardly a light could be seen anywhere below. Then, ahead, far out on the horizon, Hamish spotted a bright light sliding slowly towards them. So incredibly bright, it was quite unlike anything he had ever seen before. He watched, mystified, as it came nearer and nearer. He pointed it out to his colleagues. There are many strange phenomena in the sky that remain to be explained.

He thought of the many things he had seen from the air. The sun hanging like a huge blood red-balloon low on the horizon; the moon reflecting silver off the icecaps of Greenland; the mysterious sight of Venus rising in the dawn, brighter than any star, flashing multi-coloured through refracting layers of atmosphere; the Northern Lights over Baffin Island. But this was below them, not above — more like the searchlights and coloured marker flares he had seen over Germany. He remembered exploding bombs and exploding aircraft. Whole cities on fire lighting the night sky red and orange hundreds of miles away.

Closer and closer it came, growing ever brighter, ever clearer. It neither wavered nor did it flicker. He turned the aircraft slightly so it would pass down his side, giving him a better view.

The planet Venus is often one of the brightest lights in the sky.

But what was it? It was extraordinary, ethereal, unworldly — like a cross of gold set in the finest silver filigree.

Don't be a fool, thought Hamish. It had to be something quite ordinary. Could it be ball lightning? He had heard the stories but never seen it. No. Impossible — no thunderstorms about. He was a practical man; he certainly did not believe in flying saucers or the supernatural... but?

Then, suddenly, it became a city. Of course! He checked the chart and realised it must be Calgary. He could hardly believe it. Despite all his experience, the unusually clear atmosphere had completely fooled him. He felt he could reach out and touch it. The effect was startling, strangely mystical, sublime. Down there, far below, people were going about their lives — mothers putting children to bed, roaring traffic taking commuters home, men and women starting night shifts, lovers out on dates. But from up here?

Really! He couldn't let on to his crew how completely he had been fooled. It was only the yellow sodium lights on the major roads that glowed like gold, and the surrounding sheen of mercury-vapour streetlights that looked like silver. That was the real Calgary. Yet from high altitude, in the depth of the night, it seemed like a jewel offered up to him on a black velvet cushion. He had never seen a man-made object look so beautiful.

He knew it was an illusion, of course. Anyone who has travelled across deserts or through mountains, walked in dense fog, sailed boats or flown aircraft has experienced these illusions. On that crystal-clear night with such amazingly good visibility and with no other lights anywhere, his perception flipped between the two images — Calgary as a city and Calgary as a jewel. It was utterly entrancing. It was so incredibly and mysteriously beautiful.

He felt a touch at his shoulder. 'Captain.'

'Yes — what is it?'

One of the stewards was standing behind him. 'There's a passenger in business class who's asked to see the flight deck. What shall I tell him?'

'Tell him "no", we're busy.'

The steward retreated from the cockpit. The spell was broken. What is real? thought Hamish. Was it a transcendental moment? An exquisite jewel? Or is it a living breathing city way down below? And what could be more surreal than me, sitting here, comfortably in my shirt sleeves, rushing through the stratosphere at nearly six hundred miles an hour, in air so cold and thin I wouldn't survive an instant if I wasn't protected by this fragile aluminium tube?

He looked across at his co-pilot and flight engineer, both oblivious to these bizarre thoughts and returned to the comforting glow of the flight instruments. Yet — suddenly, over Calgary? Was he going soft? Mystical experiences only happened to the woolly-minded. Things like that didn't happen to him.

The other two had said nothing and neither would he.

Nightmares

I often sit here gazing down the river. I find it soothing after the dreams. It's quiet at three in the morning before the hubbub of the day. A few strands of mist lie along the opposite bank, obscuring the towpath. Temple Island glows dully in the moonlight. Summer is nearly over; the chill is beginning to seep into my old bones.

'You OK, Bob?'

'Yes. But can't sleep so easy these days.'

Harry, the night watchman, crunches slowly away down the gravel path with Lulu, his large placid Alsatian. They patrol the grounds and we've grown used to each other since I started having these sleepless nights.

Perhaps I should explain. The club occupies a much-extended Georgian mansion on the banks of the Thames. We moved into one of the apartments behind the main house when I grew too old to maintain the garden and Molly was still fighting cancer. It suited us well; she could play bridge, I could enjoy the reading room and the meetings with old friends. It has a good restaurant, and a bar and garden room which serves light lunches. There's always something going on — outings and special interest sections with talks on aviation, motoring, sailing, films, books and suchlike. It's a good place for a lonely old man.

The dreams started soon after Molly died. They're always the same. A man, his face swathed in rags, bursts into my room, points a gun at me and fires. There's a flash of brilliant light and I wake shivering and bathed in sweat to find I'm still alive. I was never given to dreams before. I don't hold with sleeping pills, I don't want to see the doctor — what could he do, other than prescribe more pills or send me to a shrink?

Instead, I make myself a cup of tea, watch television or go and contemplate the river until I feel sleepy again.

I'm in my mid-seventies now. I used to keep myself pretty fit — rowing, tennis and sailing — but soon after I retired my old injury came back to haunt me. I've been lame ever since. These days I walk the dog and play chess.

I try not to talk about what happened back in 1972. It's best kept suppressed in the nether regions of my brain, I guess that's the reason for my dreams. The horrifying details leap back so clearly. We were escaping from the cockpit of our VC10. George climbed through the captain's window, Ted following. While they were safely lowering themselves to the ground, I climbed through my window on the other side and started down the escape rope. As I did so, the cockpit door was flung open and the gunman rushed towards me. He fired at my head, missed and fired again. I fell to the ground, burning my hands on the rope. My leg snapped, but I managed to roll out of sight under the nose.

What followed was almost as bad. A hand grenade was flung down from the window above. Ted picked it up and threw it away into the darkness where it exploded. Some shots were fired, we were surrounded by soldiers, and I passed out.

'Bob, it's time you went back to bed, it's cold out here.' Harry is shaking my shoulder. I'm cold and stiff — half-awake. I must have drifted off. I limp slowly back across the lawn, dew soaking my feet, the moon casting long shadows across the grass. When I open the back door, Bumper, my dog, opens one eye and looks at me as though I'm daft. I make a mug of tea and slump into my favourite chair in front of the television. There's nothing worth watching.

I have only hazy memories of what happened next. It seems I drifted in and out of consciousness. An ambulance arrived to take me and the two bodies to the first-aid point. A medic gave me a shot of morphine. The next thing I knew, I was lying in bed with my leg in plaster. The doctors did their best and I remained there until an ambulance flight took me back to London where they operated to save my leg.

I know at some stage Molly came to watch over me. Ted and George came too, but that was back in London. So had the flight manager who'd flown a relief flight down to Benghazi to pick up the passengers and cabin crew. He'd also arranged the ambulance flight and for Molly to accompany it. I was grateful for that. Gradually the pieces came together. It seems the hijackers gave themselves up when they realised I couldn't fly with a broken leg. The Libyans arrested them and sent them to Cairo where they were languishing in gaol. No one really knew what they had hoped to achieve.

I wake suddenly, a cold damp nose pressing into my hand. I've been dreaming again. I put the dog out for a leak and decide, for a change, to take breakfast in the clubhouse. I need something to break the spell.

'Morning Mr Grainger, the full English?'

'No thanks, just eggs and bacon, and some coffee.'

A good walk along the river bank is what I need — something to blow away these long-suppressed recollections. But it's so hard to forget. I remember the cold hard feeling of that gun being pressed into my neck.

We'd left late that night and were northbound out of Kano on our way to Rome and London. The whole affair is engraved in my memory, despite my efforts to bury it. Middle East hijackings were at their height then, but we thought we were safe in Africa. Nevertheless, all airlines were on their guard, particularly the main flag carriers like BOAC.

Frank Bridge was the captain, a quiet man with many amusing stories about the 'old days' on flying boats. I was the senior co-pilot, with Ted Knowles navigating and George Lamb, the flight engineer — all good blokes. About an hour out of Kano, over the Sahara, there was a commotion behind me.

Suddenly that cold hard gun was pressed into my neck below my left ear, knocking my headset onto my lap. I swore and was told 'shut fuck up'. When I looked round, I could see the captain staring in amazement, also with a gun pressed into his neck. A man and a woman disappeared back into the cabin leaving three men in Arab headgear behind in the cockpit. The one beside me smelt strongly of sweat — for some reason I remember that distinctly. I reached, automatically, to put my headset back on and was shouted at again.

They were frightened and confused, shouting at each other, as well as at us. Frank remained very calm and just asked them what they wanted. The first two kept shouting, 'Cairo, Cairo, Cairo', while the third man, who was holding a grenade, seemed a little more rational. When Frank repeated his question, he leant forward and said, 'We in command now. You obey, not get hurt. Go Cairo.'

I must stop thinking like this. I finish my coffee and go to collect Bumper. He scampers around as I find his lead. The day is warming when we reach the meadow and I let him off to run around. Dogs enjoy such simple pleasures and my heart soars with his. The mist has cleared, two single sculls go down river towards the island and an eight makes a hard push back up against the current. I wish I could still do that.

I walk further than intended and find myself nearing The Trout, a pub I doubt has changed much since Queen Victoria was on the throne. The bar is dark and lined with fish and birds in glass cases. A heron eyes me fixedly from under a glass dome as I enter.

'Morning, you're early. What'll it be?'

'Pint of Brakspeare's please, and a bowl of water for the dog.'

I take the beer to a corner from where I can avoid the heron's gaze. Bumper laps his water, though he normally prefers the stronger taste of dirty puddles. The Trout is set back from the river down a narrow lane. It's well known to us locals and not plagued too much by river traffic. The anglers' bar has the virtue of welcoming dogs as well as their owners. I really shouldn't be drinking beer this early in the morning but perhaps it will help settle my thoughts.

I gaze at a few magazines which mainly contain dreary photos of damp fishermen on damp afternoons sitting huddled by river banks. I finish my beer and make my way to the gents.

'You'll have to use the ladies,' shouts the landlord from behind the bar. 'Drain's blocked. Man's coming this afternoon.'

In deference to the ladies I sit down. It's fortunate I did. The stench from next door, mixed with some type of Elsan fluid, almost knocks me out. I sit there seeing again the inside of the aircraft — it's so real I can touch it. There's blood on the cockpit floor, swarming with flies. There's no electric power, the toilets have overflowed, there's no ventilation, and people are fainting. Outside, the sand and tarmac shimmer in the heat.

I can't stay here. I pull up my trousers and stagger back to the bar.

'You OK?'

'No. I'm not. My leg's hurting abominably, must have walked too far. Could you call a taxi to take me back to the club? And tell them I have a dog.'

'How about another pint while you wait?'

'Just a half. Thanks.'

'Have it on the house. Looks like you need it.'

Back at the club, I'm dropped off by my front door, go in and make some coffee. I must get a grip. Why am I having these flashbacks? The incident in the pub has really shaken me. I sit in my old armchair and think of those events of nearly forty years ago. Smells are so evocative.

Within minutes of landing in Benghazi, the tanks ran dry, the engines died, it was that close. The lights went out, the air conditioning stopped, as the sun rose temperatures soared, and, as the day dragged on, conditions in the cabin became unbearable. Several people fainted, children were crying and an old man seemed to be having a heart attack. Memory plays such strange tricks, time became meaningless. I remember fierce arguments in Arabic; I only understood one word — Cairo, repeated many times. I pleaded with the leader, who had turned out to be the woman, to let the passengers go. She wanted fuel but the chief of police said no. We desperately needed water and, after more shouting, bottles were brought on board, but they were hardly enough. Eventually, it was agreed to release the women and children. The old man was driven away in a van. The women and children were left to walk across to the terminal.

154

Towards dusk, the temperature fell but the stench remained. People had vomited, flies buzzed everywhere, we were ragged and so were the hijackers. I hoped they wouldn't become irrational. That night I must have slept more than I realised, because dawn came quickly. The woman was still demanding fuel, the chief of police still said no. I pleaded with him but he wouldn't relent. She threatened to shoot a passenger every hour until the fuel came. A young man was made to stand at the aircraft door with a pistol held to his head. The hour went by. I can still hear now the shot and the sickening sound of his body hitting the tarmac. Still no fuel. Another passenger was selected, another hour went by, but at the last minute a fuel bowser arrived.

Around midday, the chief of police said we could leave for Cairo, provided the woman released all the remaining passengers. Eventually, after another long and heated discussion in Arabic, she agreed to release them so long as we would fly to Cairo. When the last passengers had left, I asked if the cabin crew could go too, it only needed the three of us to fly the aircraft. She said no. I prevaricated, saying we wouldn't fly unless they were released.

The stand-off lasted all afternoon. It was nearly dark when she finally let them off. I suggested we waited until dawn, so we could see to land if Cairo switched the runway lights off again. Fortunately, she saw the sense in this, so we settled down for another night, taking it in turns to doze in our seats.

I'm dozing again now. It's nearly lunchtime. I go to the kitchen to make a sandwich and return to my chair. Bumper comes to lie at my feet hoping for a crust. Soon he's asleep and beginning to twitch and whimper in the way dogs do when dreaming. I wonder what they dream about; I bet their dreams are more fun than mine.

My mind wanders back to the flight across the desert and the eventual landing at Benghazi. When I'd recovered from the initial shock, my main anxiety was fuel. Was there enough? Would they allow us to land in Cairo? Two years before, a Pan Am 747 had been hijacked to Cairo and blown up minutes after it touched down. The Egyptians might not want that to happen again. Would Ted be allowed to navigate accurately across the desert? We couldn't afford to zigzag around wasting fuel. We had to explain every move to the third man and do everything very, very slowly so he wouldn't be alarmed.

At some stage, the chief steward had managed to slip us a note saying there were two more hijackers in the cabin, both armed with guns and hand grenades. All the passengers had been ordered to the back of the aircraft, they were subdued but calm and were doing as they were told. I told him we would be in Cairo in about two hours. That meant we'd arrive before dawn.

I had been surprised that their leader was the woman. She was small, dark, lithe and oozed authority. After sending one of the gunmen back into the cabin, she spoke to me in good English. At last I had someone I could talk to. I said we'd do everything she wanted but please don't harm the passengers. I explained the limited fuel, the need to navigate accurately, and that we might not be allowed to land. She listened carefully, saying no one would be harmed so long as we did exactly what she said. The captain had been shot by mistake.

Our next problem had been navigation. Ted needed to use the periscopic sextant. We had to explain, even though it looked like a weapon, it was not and was essential for accurate navigation. She agreed and told the other hijackers to leave him be. While Ted was taking his star shots, I asked her why she was hijacking our aircraft. She was reticent, saying only they were part of the Black September Organisation, protesting against Egypt's lack of help after the Israeli athletes were killed in Munich. I felt this didn't bode well but said nothing.

Bumper has woken and is making going-out noises. I lever myself up and take him to the door. While he is out, I put the plates in the sink and make some coffee. I wish Molly were here, I need to tell her about these reawakened thoughts. She was always so calm and gentle. Bumper is scratching at the door, so I take my coffee outside to sit in the sun. He stretches out in the shade of a tree.

A 747 passes overhead, banking left towards the east, the engine note rising as it turns, then falling again when it starts to descend towards the runway. On the news this morning, the BBC ran a story on the British Airways 777 that had crashed at Heathrow two years ago, and the investigation had concluded ice in the fuel system stopped both engines. It hadn't run out of fuel as some had thought. My mind flew back to Benghazi and how nearly this had happened to us.

I remember the confusion when we neared Cairo. The woman had taken over the radio and started a long harangue in Arabic which I couldn't understand. I tried to interrupt to say if she wanted to land in Cairo, we needed to descend but she waved to me to shut up. She continued her monologue until we were nearly over Port Said. Only then did I manage to say we would soon be crossing the border into Israel. That got her attention and I turned back towards Cairo. ATC cleared us to begin a descent, but no permission to land. I said we were short of fuel and had to, they said they had switched the runway lights off so we couldn't.

The woman, I never knew her name, became very agitated, shouting at them in Arabic. I pleaded with them too, but they were adamant. We were now heading west far out over the desert in the dark, having passed Cairo once more. She wanted me to turn back; I wanted urgently to find somewhere to land. If Cairo wouldn't accept us, I knew other Egyptian airports wouldn't either. Tel Aviv was a no-no for the woman and I wasn't sure about Amman or Beirut. Cyprus was a possibility, but Benghazi seemed the best bet. I broke the impasse by opening the throttles and turning towards it. The woman threatened to shoot me. I said, 'Go ahead. If we don't land soon, we're all dead.' She relented, but it was a close call. Benghazi was about 500 miles away and we only just made it.

Waves of anxiety hit me still — my heart races. I must do something to drive these thoughts away. I feel so alone. The library doesn't close until late tonight; perhaps I can find an easy read — anything to take me out of myself. I leave Bumper behind; public libraries don't welcome dogs, and walk into town. As I pass the cinema, I look to see if they're showing something that might suit my mood; they don't, too much blood and guts. Outside the library, I meet an old friend and we discuss some of the lighter things of life, I don't tell him my woes. Then I browse the shelves and find a volume of short stories by P G Wodehouse — I hope these foolish adventures will amuse. On the way home I pass the fish and chip shop and buy some for my supper.

Bumper greets me at the door, pleased by the smell of food, he likes his share. I unwrap the cod and start to eat at the kitchen table, but I've lost my appetite — the events of the day have disturbed me too much. Bumper is in luck. I pour myself a stiff whisky and go to bed.

I was still in bed in hospital when they held Frank's funeral, so I couldn't go. I was told afterwards there'd been a huge turn-out. He was such a good man and was so looking forward to retiring to Devon. My last memories of Frank are seeing him lying, twitching on the cockpit floor, blood gushing from his mouth. He'd gone back to help Ted calculate whether we could make Cairo. I can see him now bending over the nav table — it's all so clear. There was a loud 'pop', he slumped to the floor; both gunmen stuck their pistols into my neck screaming things I didn't understand. The third man threatened to blow us up with the hand grenade. I remember vividly the absolute pandemonium and the sheer terror until things calmed down.

I sat there quivering inside. I knew I had to pull myself together. Ted and George looked shocked. I was in charge now, and everyone was looking at me. Trying to appear calm, I said, 'Please look after Frank,' and agreed to go to Cairo.

Bumper is asleep downstairs. I am lying here in the dark, the street light outside making vague patterns on the ceiling. Perhaps I should try writing all this down, it might exorcise the demons.

The Generalissimo's Lady

March in Lima, end of the rainy season, and thunderstorms had washed away part of the track. The trains weren't running, so our first idea of taking a train ride 15,000 feet up into the Andes to Ticlio was off. What else could we do? We had arrived early in the morning before dawn and now, after a short sleep, wanted to find another adventure to fill our two days off. Our captain was all for a quiet time in the hotel, as was the flight engineer. So Ian, the other co-pilot, and I were the only ones who were ready for some excitement.

We soon discovered that the town office of Trans-Peruana, a local airline, was near our hotel. What about a quick flight over the mountains instead, we thought? Yes — they had regular flights to Pucallpa and Iquitos on the other side of the Andes, seats were available, and yes — there was a flight next day which left early in the morning. We paid our money and were delighted to discover the aircraft would be an old Lockheed Constellation. As children of the jet-age, neither of us had travelled on such a venerable airliner before.

Next day, at the airport, we met the crew and asked if we could ride in the cockpit. The captain said we were welcome, but there was only one spare seat. Ian and I drew lots — I won the outbound leg, he the return.

For people who are not aviation enthusiasts, the Lockheed Constellation is a 1940s design powered by four Wright Cyclone radial piston engines. It has a distinctive curved fuselage, three tail fins and a high stalky undercarriage. As we walked out across the tarmac, I couldn't help observing the rather dilapidated appearance of this shapely beast — the red and white paintwork was bright enough, but the wings could have

One of BOAC's Lockheed L-049 Constellations.

done with a polish, and dripping oil and blackened exhaust stains on the engine cowlings prompted some second thoughts. Was it really wise to trust our lives to this ropy airline's ancient aircraft across the high Andes? The crew told us it had once belonged to BOAC. I thought of the countless flights it must have done to and fro across the Atlantic and out to the Far East — this was living history.

We climbed aboard and I made my way forward to the cockpit. My first impression was how cramped and higgledy-piggledy it all was. There were the usual seats for the captain, co-pilot and flight engineer, and a rather rickety jump seat that I eyed apprehensively. The view from the cockpit windows was limited to say the least. Then the start checks began. This was mainly a flight engineer affair. Along the bottom of his panel, below the main engine instruments, a bank of levers and switches

— throttles, mixture, superchargers, propeller controls, oil coolers, cowls, etc. and a bunch of other things I had long forgotten about. Much juggling went on, starter motors ground and whirred, the captain reached up to the magneto switches in the roof panel above his head, and the aircraft shuddered as each engine hiccupped into life. The number two on the left side was reluctant to start and needed several attempts before it staggered into action pouring out clouds of blue-grey smoke which billowed past the cockpit windows.

The whole aircraft came alive with many different vibrations and noises — so unlike the smooth quietness of the VC10 I was used to. This was a real man's aeroplane. He ran up the engines, checked the magnetos, taxied out and swung onto the runway. After a brief pause, the captain opened the throttles and, amidst more roaring and shaking, we accelerated down the runway and into the sky. We circled a couple of times to gain altitude and then set course towards the mountains, still partly wreathed in cloud. And this was where I really started

The flight deck of a Lockheed L-049 Constellation.

to have some doubts. We weaved between towering cumulus clouds, pushed through layers of stratus before bursting out into the clear with mountains filling the sky on either side. Ahead lay a saddle between snow covered peaks. And — I kid you not — the only map I could see was an Esso road map on the captain's lap. However, the crew seemed confident. We passed low over the saddle, the ground began to fall away and the long descent started down the other side towards a widening expanse of green.

Our first stop was the small town of Pucallpa. The runway was surrounded by beaten earth, grass, forest and green fields. I saw a few goats and donkeys rather too close for comfort as we taxied in towards the small terminal building. We stopped and were immediately surrounded by a great commotion of people. Sun-browned Quechua women in tall bowler hats and voluminous skirts climbed aboard with overflowing baskets of produce. There seemed no room for everyone to sit, but sit they did. Then we were off again for the next leg to Iquitos. As we turned onto the runway, a jeep ran down its length to clear away peasants, animals and chickens before we roared off into the sky again.

The next part of the flight was over what I can only describe as an interminable sea of parsley stretching from horizon to horizon — the jungle was vast. Iquitos is an improbable but fairly sizeable town set on the headwaters of the Amazon. It can be reached only by river or air, there are no roads to the outside world. As we had four hours or so before the return flight, the co-pilot and flight engineer suggested hiring a taxi to show us around. There were spacious streets and handsome Spanish colonial style buildings, but what impressed me most was the Amazon. A wide expanse of milky chocolate brown stretching out towards a thin green line of vegetation two miles away in the far distance on the other side. It was hard to believe that this water had over 2,000 miles to flow before it reached the Atlantic Ocean on the other side of the continent.

When we climbed back aboard the aircraft, Ian sat in the cockpit and I took a seat at the rear of the cabin. Motley groups of passengers began to board from the rear door, mainly peasant men and women. Not a European face among them until a very grand army officer and his lady came to sit in the row in front of me. He clearly considered himself important, being the last to board so as to make an entrance. He was tall, dressed in a dark green uniform covered with gold braid, curlicues and medals. He wore a red and white sash and a very large hat — the very image of a Spanish grandee. All he lacked was a sword! His lady was beautifully dressed in a long red skirt, closely fitting pale gold blouse and white gloves. Her skin was richly tanned, her hair almost blue-black, her neck graceful like a swan's — imagine a vision somewhere between Ava Gardner and Sofia Loren. They certainly stood out from the crowd while graciously receiving the deference due to them. Straight out of central casting!

The engines started, the aircraft shook, we taxied out, took off and headed back towards Pucallpa. I gazed out of the window

The city of Iquitos, on the Amazon, can be reached only by river or air.

at the interminable jungle below and at the sinuous brown snake of the mighty Amazon until we climbed up through some cloud. The seat belt signs were switched off. The generalissimo — as I imagined him to be — got up and went forward to the cockpit. Once he was safely out of sight, his lady leant back through the gap between the seats and asked where I was from. She spoke impeccable English but with a slight Caribbean lilt. I explained I was a pilot with BOAC and was here on a joyride. At which she said, 'Oh — so do you know Terry Flynn?'

To say I was surprised was an understatement. Then she said if she wrote him a letter would I drop it into Crew Reporting. 'Of course,' I said, and a little later she thrust a letter into my hand, asking me to make sure it got there and just had time to whisper, 'If you see him, tell him I still love him' before the generalissimo returned to the cabin.

* * *

'You guys want more cawfee?' I jumped. My story had taken me back to the Andes, to that exotic woman, her strange request and enigmatic words. The offer of coffee brought me suddenly down to earth. I nodded and the waitress filled our mugs with more of that indeterminate brown liquid which masquerades as coffee in New York. Jim Ford had remained quiet throughout my long story but, as I finished, he began to smile. I wondered why.

We were in one of those quick breakfast joints so common in the States. This one was on 48th between Lexington and 2nd, small but efficient. It had a long counter down one side behind which the chef was frying ham, bacon, eggs, hash brown potatoes, and toasting bread and English muffins, all at lightning speed. It was fairly full with customers sitting on stools along the counter and at small tables in the rest of the room. We were not far from Madison Avenue where all the advertising people worked, I guessed they were having a quick bite before starting their day in the office. Jim and I had chosen a table in the corner by the window where we could hear ourselves speak.

'Who's the easy over with hash browns?' Jim indicated it was his. 'Then yours is the sunny side up and toasted English.' She slung the plates down on the table.

'You knew Taff. Didn't you fly with him once, some time ago?' I asked between mouthfuls.

Jim looked up at the ceiling. 'Yes — a long Hong Kong trip. He was having a fling with a hostie called Amanda, nice girl, don't know why she was mixed up with a bloke like him. It was hilarious — they pretended they were newlyweds and were given the honeymoon suite in the Excelsior. Had one hell of a party, we lined the corridor outside with empty champers bottles. Remember it well, I was new and wondered whether all trips out East were like that.'

I knew about Taff Flynn and his womanising exploits, it was common knowledge round the fleet. 'Isn't he divorced now?' I asked.

Jim cut into his eggs easy over. 'Yes, and I'm not at all surprised.' And took a bite of toast. 'I lived in the same village. He moved there a few years ago. Didn't see much of each other. Saw him in the pub a few times. Had an attractive blonde wife several years younger than him. Guess she was wife number two. I was told there was a hell of a stink in the office after that Hong Kong trip, something to do with a bill for all that champers.'

The waitress came back with the jug and refilled our mugs with 'cawfee'. 'Can I have some more butter please?' I like lots of butter on my toasted English muffins — funny how you can't get them in England.

'I wonder whether it was the generalissimo's lady who did it.'

I looked at him not knowing what the hell he meant. 'Did what?' I asked.

'Made the wife run off. That girl who gave you the letter on the Connie in Peru - when was it?'

'Back in '69. Why do you ask?'

'Well — it all happened so suddenly. Must have been the middle of that same year. The village fairly buzzed with rumours. I heard all about it from his next door neighbour. It went something like this. Taff was having a nap in the back garden when this woman drove up in an open sports car and knocked on his front door. The neighbour, seeing such a film star-like creature walk up the front path, called out to Taff so he could take a look. Taff woke up, caught a fleeting glimpse as his wife let her in, shot out of his chair and hid behind some bushes at the end of the garden. He lurked in the shrubbery for a while, then asked the neighbour to help him climb over his garden fence. Taff said something about making himself scarce and needing a stiff drink so they sloped off together down to the pub.'

'But what makes you think it was the girl on the 'plane?'

'Jenny, the neighbour's wife, who had seen Taff hide and climb over the fence wondered what on earth was going on. She'd also seen the girl arrive and, being a nosy parker, decided to do some weeding in her front garden where she could have a snoop. After a while — quite a long while it seems — the lady left and she was just able to overhear something like, "When was it due?" That and you saying she still loved him makes me wonder if there's a connection.'

Perhaps I was being a bit thick, I was only half-listening because there was so much noise from the next table where two of the advertising types were discussing some deal in loud voices for all to hear.

'I wish they'd bloody shut up. D'you think she was preggers?'

'The timing fits, and the descriptions match.'

'So you think she was one of Taff's conquests, is that it?'

'Well, according to the gossip, she was tall, dark hair, well-tanned, foreign-looking and spoke with a slight Caribbean accent. Sounds very like the woman who gave you the letter in Peru, don't you think? Rumour also has it she was pregnant and didn't know Taff was married. My wife heard all about it from Jenny. She's the village gossip — and she had seen Taff's wife storm out of the house later and drive off in a shower of gravel.

'It was the publican who filled in the rest of the story. When

An aerial view of London Heathrow.

Taff returned home, he'd found his wife had locked him out — had to spend the night in the pub. Next morning the only way he could get back into his house was to burgle it. Had to borrow a ladder and climb in through the lavatory window. Jenny saw it all. She also said, next day, a furniture van rolled up and took the wife's things away. Seems she'd gone back to Mum and hasn't been seen since.'

I contemplated this news. The timing certainly fitted. I had seen the lady in March and, from what Jim had told me, the ructions in the village had happened somewhere around four months later. She must have tracked Taff down, but where she was now, no one knew. What had she been doing in Peru? Where and when had she met Taff? And why had she disappeared? If indeed it was her.

'D'you really think it was the generalissimo's lady, and not that other girl — Amanda whatsit?'

'No. Amanda's far too nicely brought up, very Home Counties — not in the least exotic. More twin set and pearls. I expect she's married now with a bunch of kids.'

I watched Jim finish his hash browns, but declined more of that awful 'cawfee'.

'Have you seen Taff since?'

'No. Shortly after all that brouhaha, he moved house. Left the village, haven't seen hide nor hair of him since.'

But I had. So I told Jim how I bumped into him at Heathrow. He was sifting through the letters in his pigeonhole in Crew Reporting. I had just flown in from Entebbe, he was on his way out — to Boston, I think.

'Did you get that letter from the lady in Peru?'

'Don't know any ladies from Peru. Never been there.' He went slightly pink. 'Must dash, got a plane to catch.' And he hurried out with his crew.

* * *

Years later, long after my conversation with Jim in New York, and quite by chance, I saw Taff again in Jamaica. He was in the coffee shop in the Pegasus Hotel when I caught sight of him with a woman whom I instantly recognised as the generalissimo's lady. She was as beautiful as ever — and Taff? He had aged well, still lean and handsome, but now with silvery hair and looking very distinguished in his captain's uniform. She was leaning forward talking earnestly, he was sipping coffee and looking slightly sheepish. And there between them was a young lad of about ten or twelve tucking into an ice cream. He had a slight look of Taff about him, it was the hair, I think.

The rest of his crew were gathering in the foyer waiting for the crew bus. One of them called out to say the bus had arrived and I just had time to duck out of sight as Taff rose to leave. I watched him pat the boy on the shoulder and give the woman a quick peck on the cheek. Then he left them to join the others on the bus.

Hmmm, I thought, perhaps a chicken has come home to roost.

The Golden Gryphon

Something sharp poking into my back. The floor cold, hard, unyielding. Metal. Dark. Hiss of air conditioning. Small winking lights in some kind of racks. Don't move, whatever you do, don't move. It's all electrical.

Heavy tramp of boots overhead. They're looking for me. Shrink back further. In the corner, here. Count to a hundred. An age. Boots moving away. Don't move. Will they come back? Another age.

Trapdoor thrown open. Blinding light. 'Out, quick as you can.' Not one of them. Epaulets. Pushed up the circular staircase. Hurry, hurry. Bundled into a recess. Coats. Briefcase thrown over my feet.

'Don't move. We'll bluff our way out.'

The sound of shouting comes up from below. Someone enters the cockpit and the crew start their pre-flight checks. In a surreal moment, the litany of checks and responses transports me straight back to school.

'Oxygen.' — 'Checked, 100 per cent.'

'O Lord, open thou our lips — and our mouths shall shew forth thy praise.'

'INSs.' — 'Nav mode. Loading checked.'

'Briefing.' — 'As stated, after take-off at 750 feet, turn left onto zero zero two degrees.',

'O God, make speed to save us. O Lord, make haste to help us.'

'QNH.' — 'One zero zero nine. Set and cross checked.'

'Take-off data.' — 'Checked, indexed and bugged.'

'O Lord, shew thy mercy upon us. And grant us thy salvation.'

Someone else enters the cockpit. The army officer. She sees

his shoes through a gap between the coats. He's only inches away. Will he look in the wardrobe?

'OK Capitano, now can go.'

'What were you looking for?'

'Ees better not ask.'

I ease my legs, trying not to disturb the coats. The sound of his footsteps fades. I hear him go downstairs, my prayers are answered. Only hours before I was in the British Embassy. Best to forget the events of the last few days. The nightmares are still too raw. And now this.

* * *

She knew nothing of the chain of events behind the scenes after she had sought refuge in the embassy. She was told only that she would be put on that night's flight to London. One of the attachés — investment or trade — she thought, had signalled the Foreign and Commonwealth Office and things had gone from there. The FCO then contacted British North Atlantic Airlines who, in turn, briefed the captain of the next flight through Simón Bolívar Airport. He should expect a passenger to board the aircraft ahead of all the others and not to ask any questions. 'It's all above board,' they said. At much the same time, the man from the embassy spoke to the BNAA station manager asking his help to arrange for a female passenger to board the aircraft in secret during the turnaround. Together, they worked on a plan to drive her out in a catering van and seat her in the upper deck cabin of the Boeing 747.

* * *

Several hours before and five hundred miles away in Barbados, Captain John Carter had just dropped off for an afternoon nap before taking the evening flight down to Caracas when the telephone rang beside his bed. Damn it, he thought, don't they know not to ring when I'm trying to sleep.

'Call from London, Sir,' said the switchboard. 'Putting you

through now.' And then the familiar voice of the flight manager. 'That you, John? Sorry to disturb you, but it's rather important. Are you alone?' He retrieved the handset from where he'd dropped it on the floor and mumbled a reply.

'We've just had a call from the FCO. When you're in Caracas, they want to bring a passenger on board before all the others, someone called Sam Holden. So far as you are concerned, treat it as normal and don't ask any questions. Whoever it is will be seated on the upper deck. This is all very confidential and it is official, you'll have to find some way of squaring it with the rest of the crew. Tell 'em as little as possible. Only you and the station manager are in the know.'

John had heard about these situations, they had happened before but this was a first for him. He lay awake wondering who the mystery bloke was and why he was being smuggled out of the country. 'Exfiltration' they called it. He decided it would be best to play it by ear; see what the station manager said and hope everything would all go smoothly.

Simón Bolívar International Airport, Maiquetía, Vargas, Venezuela.

At the embassy, Samantha answered the knock on her door. The attaché came in. A plump man, rather nondescript, he could easily have passed for a bank clerk. 'OK, it's all fixed. You leave tonight on the evening flight after dark. You'll need to wear these,' he handed her a white blouse and some dark blue slacks. 'We've checked your size, they should fit. Oh — and you'll need to wear your hair up.'

After he had gone, she looked at herself in the bathroom mirror. Neither her soft brown eyes nor her oval face conveyed any of the strain she had been under. The tan, acquired during her weeks in the mountains, hid any pallor there might have been. She was a small woman, barely five foot four, but her spare frame concealed a hidden strength — the result of years of training. She wondered how best to manage her hair. Normally, she wore it in a ponytail, she would have to find some way of coiling it up — she would only cut it off if she had to. She remembered how good she looked at embassy parties in a red dress with her dark hair flowing down her back. It fitted her Spanish persona. She put on the clothes and used some hairpins borrowed from the attaché's wife. The effect was not as she liked, but it would have to do.

The attaché came for her at six o'clock and, taking her out via a back door, ushered her into the enclosed courtyard where his car was parked. It was an old Ford, somewhat battered around the edges. It smelt strongly of tobacco, there was a hole in the seat, and the carpet was worn and dirty.

'You'll have to crouch down there under this rug until we leave town,' he said. 'I don't want anyone to see you.'

'But it will mess up my outfit.'

'Can't be helped, we can sort that out later at the airport.'

She used the rug to keep off the dirt and squeezed into the front footwell beside the driver. The attaché drove at a sedate pace so as not to attract attention. Once clear of the city, they moved onto the highway towards the mountains, where it began to rain. In the dark and the rain and the mist, the attaché said it was safe to come out from under the rug. She tidied her hair as best she could.

'You OK?' he asked. 'I'd better brief you on what we'll do next. The station manager will be waiting for us with an airline jacket and a hat. You'll need to put those on before you leave the car. I won't come with you, but he'll take you through the terminal straight into their offices. Anyone watching will think you're a ground hostess or something. This rain will help too. Just follow the manager and look as though you know exactly what you are doing. Got it?'

'How will I get out to the aircraft?'

'Paul, he's the manager, he'll look after you. He's thought it all through. He'll take you out in a catering van and say you're from head office, come to report on catering uplifts. The captain's been briefed too. You'll look exactly like someone who's supposed to be there. The main thing is, look confident.'

They drew up near one end of the terminal building. Paul was waiting for them. He slid in beside her and gave her a jacket with the airline's logo on the breast pocket and a ground hostess's hat. She tucked her hair fairly neatly into it and followed him through the terminal. They weaved their way through the usual hubbub of people, children and baggage trolleys. They bypassed the long queue of passengers at check-in, ducked behind the counter and in through a door to the office behind.

A teleprinter was clacking away in the corner, telephones were ringing and several staff were counting through reams of paper. 'Come this way,' said Paul and led her into a side office. 'You'll do. The jacket covers your blouse nicely. Take this clipboard, hold it under your arm when we go out, it'll make you look official. It's amazing, you can fool anyone with a clipboard!' And he gave her an encouraging smile.

'See that door over there? It leads out to a corridor and then onto the apron where all the service vehicles are. I'll check to see if the catering van's there, then we'll drive out to the aircraft. No one'll see us in the rain and we'll go up the steps on the far side away from the terminal. That's where we load the catering. I'll take you up and introduce you to the captain. He's expecting you.

So far as the rest of the crew go, you're making an informal inspection of the catering uplift. All you have to do is watch what comes on board and pretend to take notes. Here are the forms, just scatter a few ticks in these boxes.

'It's nothing unusual, people are always coming out from head office to check on things like this. Bloody nuisance sometimes, keep getting in the way. When you've done that for a while, go upstairs and take a seat at the front of the upper deck cabin. Make it look as though you're writing a report. When the passengers start to board, go forward to the cockpit and sit on the jump seat — it's the one on the left behind the captain.'

Paul finished his quick brief and left her in the office while he checked the coast was clear. Sam studied the forms and watched as people came and went. At times, there seemed to be more paperwork than people. A man with an oil company logo on his shirt came in and asked for the final fuel figure. He was dripping wet and left puddles on the floor. A woman poked her head into the office and asked Sam how many first class meals? Sam said to ask Paul, 'he's just popped outside.'

Paul came back. 'Thirteen,' he told the woman, then to Sam, 'Follow me.'

They went down a dingy corridor which ran along behind a row of offices and came to a locked door. Paul punched a code into the key pad to release the lock and they went outside onto the apron. A blue and white van was parked near the door and there, beyond it and a melee of baggage carts and tugs, stood the aircraft. Safety at last!

'Jump in, I'll drive us round to the far side.' He threaded his way adroitly past the scattered vehicles and stopped at the foot of the steps. They dashed up to avoid the rain and entered the galley area.

'This is Sam, she's here to check the catering. I'll take her up to see the captain. Know where he is?'

'Up in the cockpit.' The steward stepped aside to let them past. Sam gave him a quick smile, waved the clipboard and followed Paul up the circular staircase to the upper deck.

'Best sit there when you write your report.' He indicated a seat by the windows on the left side. 'Just keep looking busy. They may even bring you a cup of tea.' And he slipped away.

Sam busied herself with the sheaf of papers on her clipboard. She made some notes. Looked pensive. Inspected the upstairs galley, and the one down below on the main deck. Made some more fictitious notes. She sat down again, gratefully accepted the cup of tea — and waited. The refuelling man bounced up the stairs and into the cockpit, leaving a trail of water behind him. 'Fuelling all done, Capitano,' he announced. One of the crew, equally wet, checked the figures, signed the log and showed it to the captain. Sam sipped her tea and glanced out of the window. 'Oh shit, just when I thought I was safe.' A squad of soldiers were marching out from behind the terminal building.

'Oh shit!' In the cockpit, Captain Carter watched them encircle the aircraft. 'Look what's coming our way.' Grabbing his hat, he leapt out of his seat and told the flight engineer, 'That woman, the one who's checking the catering, she's sitting on the upper deck. Quick, put her in the coal hole; I'll explain later.' And dashed downstairs.

'Follow me.' Sam did as she was told.

Downstairs, the captain went back to door two left. Fortunately, they were using that door and not the one at the front. He confronted the officer in charge of the soldiers, asking what the devil they wanted. Meanwhile, the flight engineer ripped back the carpet in the first-class cabin to reveal a trap door in the floor.

'In there and keep quiet.'

Sam dropped down into the cavity beneath the floor. It wasn't far but she grazed her shin on the steps trying to avoid the radio racks on either side. The flight engineer slammed the trap door shut. It was dark, disorientating and very uncomfortable.

* * *

Back in the cockpit again, Captain Carter turned to his co-pilot and flight engineer and beckoned them closer. 'Listen carefully. I had to let those soldiers in and we had to act fast. Now we must look normal. That catering woman is being smuggled out by the British Embassy. I don't know why, that's not for us to know. The soldiers are searching for her, but we'll keep her in the avionics bay until after take-off. To hell with the rules. We'll just get on with things as though nothing's happening.'

The army officer in charge climbed the circular staircase, ordered two of his soldiers to search the upper deck and the toilets and marched forward into the cockpit. His English was not good. 'Where you hef woman on aeroplano?'

'Only my crew, there's no one else.'

Fortunately, Paul appeared at that moment and spoke to the officer in Spanish.

'Bueno! We now look all other place.'

As he ushered the officer out, Paul leant back to the flight engineer, 'I'll escort them around the outside and show 'em the holds. When they've gone, I'll give you the thumbs up.'

John looked at his colleagues. 'Phew. That was close. OK, where were we? Fuel's loaded, passengers'll be here soon. I guess Paul will delay them until the soldiers have gone. I wonder what that girl did to cause all this fuss.'

'Call on the intercom, Skipper,' said the flight engineer. 'Paul says they've found the outside hatch into the avionics bay and want to look inside.'

'Oh fuck!' He paused. 'I know — tell Paul to tell the soldiers only the flight engineer is allowed to open it. Then go outside and delay them while I get the girl out.'

The flight engineer ran down the steps onto the tarmac and fiddled with the locks of the external hatch behind the nosewheel. 'They're a bit stiff,' he explained. At the same time, the captain shot downstairs into the first-class cabin, pulled back the carpet, opened the trap door and told Sam to climb out quickly. 'Run upstairs while I close it again.'

He followed her up, pushed her into the crew wardrobe at the back of the cockpit and hid her behind the crew jackets. As a final touch, he hid her feet with a briefcase.

'Don't move. We'll bluff our way out.'

The flight engineer came back into the cockpit. 'They're going now, they've searched the holds and the coal hole. I've closed the outside hatch and smoothed the carpet in first class. Reckon we're ready for the before start checks now, don't you?' he grinned.

He picked up the checklist folder, 'OK then. First item — oxygen.'

'Checked, 100 per cent.'

'INSs'

'Nav mode, loading checked,' came the response. 'I'll read out the first three waypoints.' And, again, the litany began.

Part way through, the army officer reappeared and sneered gruffly, 'OK Capitano, now can go.'

Outside in the rain, Paul gave them a discreet thumbs up

The electronics and engineering bay (coal hole) of a Boeing 747 can be accessed via a trapdoor on the main deck.

as he gave the order to board the passengers. When the doors were closed, and the engines started, the flight engineer moved the coats and helped a very cramped Sam out of the wardrobe. 'Leave your jacket and hat here. Wait until we're out by the runway, then go back. There's a seat reserved for you on the upper deck, Jane will show you where.'

* * *

The engine note rose, the aircraft accelerated and Sam sat in her seat waiting for lift off. It seemed a long, long time before the vibration ceased and they were airborne. She felt safe at last, they couldn't get her now, or could they? Sam had heard of cases when Air Traffic Control had ordered aircraft to land. Surely they wouldn't do that now? Not after all this.

Jane, the upper deck stewardess, went forward with some mugs of tea for the flight crew. Sam watched her come back. 'The captain says we are well away now, he thought you might need one of these.' And on a little silver tray, she handed Sam a very large gin and tonic with ice and lemon. The glass was beaded with moisture.

Sam had never seen anything so good. She took a sip and then drained the glass in a most unladylike manner. And there, stuck to the bottom of the glass, much magnified by the shape of the base, she could see a paper coaster with the airline's logo — a Golden Gryphon on a dark blue shield.

'Like another?'

'Yes, please. You've no idea how good it is to see your Golden Gryphon.'

* * *

Up in the cockpit, as they climbed through 20,000 feet, John turned to his co-pilot and flight engineer, 'Thanks, you two — I hope I never, *ever,* have to do that again.'

Morning Arrival

Captain Ian McLeod takes his customary walk around the cabin. He talks to some of the passengers who are still awake, smooths the ruffled feathers of a man in first class who is complaining about the service, stops at each of the galleys to see how the cabin crew are faring and tells them they will be arriving in London ahead of schedule, warns of the turbulence forecast near Ireland and, over a cup of coffee, discusses with David, the senior cabin crew member, the best time for serving breakfast — before or after the turbulence? But forecasts are so inaccurate they decide to play it by ear.

He climbs the spiral staircase to the upper deck and goes forward to the cockpit. He is a tall spare man, in his late fifties. He slides into the pilot's seat, stooping low to avoid the switches on the overhead panel. His round face and bald head, surrounded by a frieze of white hair, give him the air of a benign cleric. He needs half-moon glasses to read the small print on aeronautical charts; when wearing these way from the cockpit, despite his height, he could easily be mistaken for Chesterton's Father Brown.

Now, settling comfortably back at the controls, he never fails to be surprised by how small the cockpit is, so snug compared with the main deck. Everything to hand — multiple switches, dials, levers and lights, all within comfortable reach. He decides to look again through the Met folder — a sheaf of papers showing the upper level winds and temperatures, the position of the jet stream and the surface forecast for the UK airports. Chris, the co-pilot, takes off his headset and passes him the latest weather reports. 'Heathrow's still pretty murky, so are the other London airports. Manchester and Birmingham look better. Prestwick's OK, but I missed the others, too much interference on HF tonight.' HF is the High Frequency long-range radio used when out over the ocean.

Approaching longitude 30 west, the mid-point in the North Atlantic, the flight engineer shows him the latest fuel check. 'Five hundred up, Boss, there's easily enough to hold for a while before we have to divert.'

'Thanks, Len.'

When they left New York, the weather forecast was OK — not good, but adequate. Since then the visibility has deteriorated and the cloud base is now lower — Heathrow is on limits, barely enough to see to land. They have one autopilot unserviceable which means they cannot do an automatic landing. Being a prudent man, Ian loaded extra fuel before leaving New York. He is pleased the jet stream is faster than forecast; arriving early means he will have a little more fuel than planned, enough to wait in the holding pattern for at least 45 minutes before he has to divert to Birmingham, rather less if he decides to go to Prestwick.

Oh, well, we'll just have to wait and see. The more immediate problem is the turbulence. The air is still smooth, but over Ireland, the jet stream is due to take a sudden turn to the north. In his mind's eye, Ian can see this river of air, high in the sky, swirling around the globe and rushing across the Atlantic. Ever since leaving the Canadian coast, it has been boosting them along at an extra 150 knots. The passengers will be pleased to arrive in London ahead of schedule but they won't like their breakfast being delayed by turbulence.

The problem with jet streams is that when you leave the core, and particularly where they bend, the smooth high-speed air mixing with the slower air on either side causes multiple eddies almost exactly like the little whirlpools you see in a river on either side of fast-flowing water. And this will be almost exactly when David and his team would like to serve breakfast. Hot coffee flying into people's laps is best avoided. On the other hand, there might be no turbulence at all. I think we'd better wait, muses Ian.

'Tea anyone?' Sandra, the upper deck stewardess, comes in with three mugs of tea. 'Black, no sugar, for you, captain, milk and sugar for Chris and here's another without sugar for Len. Anything else I can bring you?' And she leaves as quietly as she entered.

What a lovely girl, thinks Ian, so like my daughter, much the same age too. So considerate and kind, brings us tea exactly when we need it. Funny how aeroplanes run on kerosene and pilots run on tea. I wonder what strange alchemy makes some crews gel and others not? Most of us work well together, but some merely tolerate each other. This crew, however, has a rare understanding. None of us have flown together before and are unlikely to do so again — airline life is like that. We only met a week ago but here we are working as one with a harmony that warms my heart. I wish it was always like this.

His crew knows it is Ian who has created this harmony. He sips his tea and leans his face against the side window, the better to see the stars. All clear above. There's Polaris way out on the left with the W of Cassiopeia beyond. Yes, and there's Capella too, a little to the west, low down on the horizon, exactly where it should be. So like that picture by Van Gogh, the one at Arles, where the stars stand out like dinner plates in the sky. Ian knows they aren't really like that, but they feel like it — they're so clear and bright. High up here in the atmosphere the Milky Way feels so close he can almost reach out and hold it. Night is so special — mysterious, infinite, timeless continuity.

Below, a solid sheet of cloud shines white like snow, lit by the moon behind. How tranquil it looks yet he knows it hides a torrent of air, rushing them eastward.

Suddenly, ahead, a bright light flashes out from behind the clouds — red, white, green — blue, orange, yellow — every colour imaginable. An aircraft? Certainly not. Ian glances at the compass. Venus rising in the east. He has seen her so many times before, climbing slowly towards her rightful place in the coming dawn. Coyly, she hides for a moment behind a band of stratus, then re-emerges, now dressed in modest brilliant white, all playfulness forgotten.

Chris, head down, hands clamped over his headphones, misses the display ahead. He is waiting for the answering call from Shanwick Oceanic Control. Reception is poor, static crackles in his ears making it hard to hear the distant voice of the controller in southern Ireland. 'Shanwick, Shanwick, Shanwick, you are breaking up, say again, say again,' he shouts. Then, faintly through the interference, the acknowledgement comes, they have received his 30 west position report. All is well.

Outside, Venus is high now, shining clear and bright. The other stars are beginning to fade in the approaching dawn. Thin strands of cirrus glow pink. Far below, thick stratus stretches darkly out towards the horizon. The moon has vanished. Soon, the sun will turn it all to gold.

In the cockpit, all is peaceful, lit only by the dim lights from the many instruments, the only sounds the soft swish of airflow past the windscreen and the distant hum of engines. Three men working in harmony, secure in their knowledge, secure in the air. Soon, they will go their separate ways — in different crews flying to different places in different parts of the world.

David comes into the cockpit. 'How's it looking?'

'Another half hour and it'll be daylight. Still planning on breakfast in an hour?'

'Ideally, yes.'

'You'll need to be quick. I reckon the turbulence will start soon. Don't think you really have time. Better start now.'

'But they've only just finished dinner, I'd prefer to wait.'

'OK, your decision, but I think it'll be quite bumpy. I may need you to stop. Just make sure everything's well stowed and I'll keep you posted'

That's all they can do for the moment, and he turns back to contemplate the horizon ahead. Curls of cirrus, still pink but turning grey, lie wickedly overhead and along the horizon. Signposts in the sky. Is that the edge of the jet stream where it turns? Suddenly the sun bursts out from behind the clouds, stabbing his eyeballs with shards of light. He hooks the North

Atlantic chart over the plastic sunshade to blot it out. At this ghastly hour in the morning, stabs in the eyeballs are not welcome.

He continues to scan the clouds ahead. Despite being warm and snug here in this peaceful cockpit, in his bones, he knows he needs to be cautious. 'Give the Pan Am ahead a call on VHF, would you? Ask them what the ride is like? Any turbulence? That sort of thing.' Chris does so and Pan Am reports 'as smooth as a baby's bottom'. But Ian still does not like it.

A slight tremor runs through the aircraft, then a rumble, as though driving over cobblestones — not enough to worry him. Uncomfortable, but certainly not dangerous. Perhaps an indication of rough air to come. He switches on the seat belt signs. David is right to delay breakfast.

'I'll ask Shanwick if they have any reports,' says Chris. No — nothing serious, only some light chop, the controller replies. The cobblestones continue; irritating but enough to slop Ian's tea. No matter, it's gone cold.

They pass 20 west, then 15 west. Within range of Shannon, they change frequency to call on VHF. Shannon identifies their position on radar, a lower level is available if they would like it. Once again, Ian weighs his options. The turbulence is still only slight. If we stay here, it could get worse. If we descend now, we'll burn more fuel. I might want that fuel in case we have to hold before landing. The passengers won't like it if we have to divert. He does a quick calculation; 40 minutes to top of descent, 30 minutes descending towards London, 10 minutes for the approach, that leaves 30 minutes holding before we must divert to Prestwick — more if Birmingham is OK. He makes his mind up. 'Ask ATC for a descent to Flight Level two nine zero (29,000 feet); the Met chart says the core is at 35. I don't think we'll use much extra fuel lower down.'

Descending through 33,000 feet, there is a sharp lurch, several quite violent bumps followed by a long drawn out rumble, and then — smooth air. Will there be more? You never can tell. Ian decides to leave the seat belt signs switched on.

He calls David on the interphone and says to start breakfast but take care with hot liquids. Again, he mulls his options. The Heathrow cloud base is only 300 feet, visibility around 600 metres. Shouldn't be a problem, but much will depend on how many other aircraft are waiting to land; it's the busy time of the morning. Ian checks his charts and familiarises himself with the route to Manchester — just in case. Always wise to be ready for all eventualities. He briefs his crew on the landing procedures and his intended route should they need to divert.

Over South Wales, they start down. The cloud below looks so solid he feels he could walk on it. Passing 20,000 feet, some wisps flit past the cockpit windows. Then they are in it. The sun is left behind. The ride is smooth. Ian knows it will be like this all the way down — stratus is like that. It gets darker as they descend.

David calls with an update on the cabin, the breakfast things are being hastily tidied away ready for landing. Some of the passengers are complaining they've hardly had time to finish and there's no time to go to the loo. The bombastic businessman in first class is berating the chief steward because he's had

The former London Air Traffic Control Centre at West Drayton.

to rush his breakfast. Really, it's most inconsiderate, what does the captain think he's doing? He should have avoided all that turbulence. The chief steward, ever the diplomat, tries to explain that it is always difficult to avoid. However, the jet stream has given them a much faster flight than usual. He is sure 'Sir' will be pleased to arrive early.

'Tell the captain I want to see him.' The chief steward, knowing the captain is busy, explains it is not possible. 'Then tell him I shall write to the chairman to complain.' He hides a smile and, in all seriousness, assures 'Sir' that that's a very good idea. He fetches him some company notepaper and a pen.

Down, down they descend through layer after layer of cloud — darker and darker as the altimeter unwinds. They pass Woodley, near Reading, and are cleared to Ockham to enter the holding stack at Flight Level one two zero (12,000 feet). Ockham is near Woking, fifteen miles or so south of Heathrow. It is one of the four holding areas that feed aircraft into the airport. There, they will have to circle in an oval pattern, descending in steps of a thousand feet, as each aircraft ahead is cleared to land.

'Only 25 minutes of fuel before we need to divert, captain,' says the flight engineer. Just enough, thinks Ian, but it will be tight. Gradually, ATC clears them down step by step until, at 7,000 feet, they are told to change frequency and call approach control. They breathe a collective sigh of relief as they head off towards the north-west to start their approach. They are cleared to descend to 3,500 feet and turn right onto a heading of zero six zero to intercept the localiser — the radio beam of the instrument landing system (ILS) that will guide them towards the runway.

Ian sets up the autopilot for an automatic approach so that, first, it will lock onto the radio beam towards the runway and, then, automatically descend on the radio glideslope down towards the runway threshold. 'Speedbird five one two, cleared ILS approach, runway zero nine right, RVR 600 metres,' and the radar controller gives them the frequency to call the control tower for landing clearance.

'My thrust levers.' Ian carefully reduces the power on the four engines to control the speed as they start to descend on the glidepath. He calls for undercarriage down, for landing flap and the landing checklist. Chris actions each item in turn, as Len reads the checklist to ensure everything has been completed ready for landing.

Ian steadies the aircraft at the right airspeed. Passing 1,000 feet, the tower controller clears them to land on runway zero nine right. The wind is five knots from the north-east. But the visibility is now only 600 metres.

Increasing drizzle smears the windscreen and streams aft along the glass in little rivulets. The cloud grows darker and darker, the altimeter slowly unwinds through 500 feet, 400 feet, 300 feet, '100 above,' calls Chris. A few lights begin to appear through the murk. Car headlights, then the white centre lights of the approach lighting system, followed by the cross bars, and then — the first of the runway lights. 'Decision height,' he calls. 'Continuing,' replies Ian. He disengages the autopilot, fixes his gaze upon the aiming point on the runway. They slide over the threshold lights, Ian raises the nose a few degrees and slowly reduces the power. The engine noise dies away and the aircraft settles onto the runway. He pulls the speedbrake lever to raise the spoilers along the top of the wings and selects reverse thrust. The engines roar. Len reaches forward beneath Ian's hands to subtly adjust the power. Chris calls, '80 knots' and Ian gently cancels reverse thrust and slows the giant aircraft to a walking pace.

They are down on a cold dank February morning. The windscreen wipers beat back and forth. Green centre line lights on the taxiway guide them to the parking apron where they shut down the engines, complete their final checks, fold away their charts and write up the logs — the voyage report, communications logs and maintenance book.

As they tidy up the flight deck, they are thinking of home. Ian, not far off retirement, is looking forward to seeing his new grandchild. Len, a keen metal worker in his spare time, after a good afternoon sleep, plans to go down to his workshop and bore out the cylinder of the steam engine he is making to power his boat. Chris just wants to put his feet up and watch the Five Nations rugby match on television. David will be pleased to spend a few days with his wife on a short break in Paris. They will all go their separate ways and may only meet again by chance in some faraway place when they next fly.

On his way home, Ian watches the streams of traffic driving into London; busy people on their way to boring offices. He does not envy them. Instead, he feels a little smug, a feeling enjoyed by most who have been up through the night and have finished their day's work. He contemplates the hundreds of times he has flown into Heathrow and the thousands of people he has carried safely around the world. Have they any idea of the vastness of the skies? The power of the elements? Jet streams roaring round the globe faster than anything found on the surfaces of the earth? Great castles of roiling thunderclouds over 10 miles high near the equator in India, Africa and South America? And everywhere, the thin air and Antarctic temperatures outside the fragile aluminium skin of their 747?

Ian and his crew have the quiet satisfaction of knowing their duty of care brought everyone safely home. But his passengers? What will they remember of their flight today? A slightly bumpy ride, a late breakfast, and little time to eat it. Perhaps that businessman will even write to the chairman complaining about the pilot. What does he know about the oceans of air above his head?

In 2019, to mark their 100th anniversary, British Airways repainted a Boeing 747-400 in BOAC's iconic blue and gold livery.